W9-DIZ-806

Introduction to

THERMODYNAMICS OF IRREVERSIBLE PROCESSES

Second Edition

Introduction to

THERMODYNAMICS OF IRREVERSIBLE PROCESSES

Second, Revised Edition

By I. PRIGOGINE

University of Brussels
Brussels, Belgium

Interscience Publishers,
a division of John Wiley & Sons
New York • London

Library of Congress Catalog Card Number 61-12683

PRINTED IN THE UNITED STATES OF AMERICA

Preface to the First Edition

A serious limitation of classical thermodynamics as a general tool for the macroscopic description of physicochemical processes lies in the fact that its method is based on such concepts as "reversible processes" and "true equilibrium states."

It is now generally recognized that in many important fields of research a state of true thermodynamic equilibrium is only attained in exceptional conditions. Experiments with radioactive tracers, for example, have shown that the nucleic acids contained in living cells continuously exchange matter with their surroundings. It is also well known that the steady flow of energy which originates in the sun and the stars prevents the atmosphere of the earth or stars from reaching a state of thermodynamic equilibrium.

Obviously then, the majority of the phenomena studied in biology, meteorology, astrophysics and other subjects are irreversible processes which take place outside the equilibrium state.

These few examples may serve to illustrate the urgent need for an extension of the methods of thermodynamics so as to include irreversible processes. Such a generalization is all the more important because the general microscopic theory of irreversible processes is still in its initial stages.

In this book I shall try to present a short and simple account of recent developments in the thermodynamics of irreversible processes. In order to produce a self-contained text most of the results of classical thermodynamics which have an immediate bearing on the subject, and especially the two fundamental laws, have been briefly reformulated. It is therefore not necessary for the reader to be fully acquainted with classical thermodynamics, although a certain familiarity with its methods will certainly facilitate understanding of the text.

Brief though its history may be, the thermodynamic theory of irreversible processes has already led to a large number of applications which could not be dealt with fully within the restricted space of this book. I have therefore tried to select the most characteristic and illuminating examples rather than to attempt a complete treatment. In this way I hope to serve the purpose of this volume, which is simply to introduce the reader to the latest developments in the already vast province of thermodynamics, and to stimulate him into taking up a more detailed study of the subject.

For a fuller account the reader may be referred to my earlier book: *Etude Thermodynamique des Phénomènes Irréversibles* (1947) or to the excellent monograph by de Groot, *Thermodynamics of Irreversible Processes* (1951). A complete list of references may be found in these books. A very good account of the applications of thermodynamics of irreversible processes may also be found in the review article by R. Haase, *Ergeb. exakt. Naturw.*, vol. 26, p. 56 (1952).

I am indebted to my collaborators, Dr. P. Mazur, Dr. N. Trappeniers and Dr. G. Klein, for their revision of the English text.

I. Prigogine

Brussels, Belgium

Preface to the Second Edition

Since the appearance of the first edition of this book in 1955, no fundamental progress has been achieved in the thermodynamics of irreversible processes. For this reason, the only modifications introduced herein are the addition of Paragraph 6 to Chapter V dealing with "continuous systems, and the replacement of the appendix in the first edition by Chapter VII, which deals with non-linear problems. Much remains to be done in this area of non-linear problems and the reader may refer to two review papers by Th. A. Bak and S. Ono in *Advances in Chemical Physics*, Volume 3, 1961, for further details.

In recent years a great deal of progress has been achieved in the statistical treatment of non-equilibrium processes. One may expect that ultimately this will have repercussions on the development of phenomenological thermodynamic methods. However, a discussion of these statistical aspects is outside the scope of this small book. A detailed exposition may be found in the book, *Non-Equilibrium Statistical Mechanics*, by the author.

I. Prigogine

Brussels, Belgium

Contents

CHAPTER IV

General Statements Concerning Entropy Production and Rates of Irreversible Processes

CHAPTER V

The Phenomenological Laws—Interference of Irreversible Processes

CHAPTER VI

The Stationary Non-Equilibrium States

CHAPTER VII

Non-Linear Problems

Introduction to

THERMODYNAMICS OF IRREVERSIBLE PROCESSES

Second Edition

CHAPTER I

Conservation of Mass in Closed and Open Systems

1. Isolated, Closed and Open Systems

The systems to which we shall apply the methods of thermodynamics are formed by the contents of a well defined geometrical volume of macroscopic dimensions.

The boundary of such a volume is a mathematical surface which separates the outside world, or more simply "the exterior," from the system.

It is useful to classify thermodynamic systems according to the exchanges of energy (heat and work) and matter through their boundaries. We shall distinguish between *isolated systems* which can exchange neither energy nor matter, *closed systems* which exchange energy but no matter and *open systems* which exchange both energy and matter with the exterior.

Classical thermodynamics has been concerned mainly with the study of closed systems. One striking achievement of recent developments has been to withdraw this limitation so as to generalize the methods of thermodynamics to open systems which are of great importance for biological thermodynamics as well as for many other fields such as meteorology and geology.

2. Extensive and Intensive Properties

Properties like mass m and volume V are defined by the system as a whole and called extensive properties or variables. It is clear that such variables are additive: for example, the total mass of the system is equal to the sum of the masses of its different parts.

On the other hand, the pressure p or the temperature T take well defined values at each point of the system and are therefore called intensive properties or variables.

3. Conservation of Mass in Closed Systems

We consider a closed system containing c components ($\gamma = 1 \ldots c$) among which a simple chemical reaction is possible. In a closed system any variation in the masses will result only from the chemical reaction. Thus the change of the mass m_γ of component γ during the time interval dt can be written as

$$dm_\gamma = \nu_\gamma M_\gamma d\xi \tag{1.1}$$

where M_γ is the molar mass of component γ and ν_γ its stoichiometric coefficient in the chemical reaction. This coefficient is counted positive when γ appears in the right-hand member of the reaction equation, negative when it appears in the left-hand member; ξ is the degree of advancement or extent of reaction introduced by Th. De Donder [1–5].

As an example we consider the reaction

$$N_2 + 3H_2 \rightarrow 2NH_3$$

According to (1.1), we have

$$\frac{dm_{N_2}}{-M_{N_2}} = \frac{dm_{H_2}}{-3M_{H_2}} = \frac{dm_{NH_3}}{2M_{NH_3}} = d\xi$$

The total mass of the system is given by $m = \sum_\gamma m_\gamma$. Summing (1.1) over γ, the principle of conservation of mass for a closed system is expressed by

$$dm = (\sum_\gamma \nu_\gamma M_\gamma) d\xi = 0 \tag{1.2}$$

The equation

$$\sum_{\gamma} \nu_{\gamma} M_{\gamma} = 0$$

is called the equation of the chemical reaction or, more briefly, the stoichiometric equation.

Instead of the mass of the component it is often useful to consider the mole numbers $n_1 \ldots\ldots n_c$. We then have

$$dn_{\gamma} = \nu_{\gamma} d\xi \tag{1.3}$$

Equation (1.1) or (1.3) introduces the extent of reaction ξ. Per unit time

$$\mathrm{v} = \frac{d\xi}{dt} \tag{1.4}$$

which defines the chemical reaction rate. It is the ratio between the increment $d\xi$ and the interval of time dt. According to (1.3) and (1.4) the increase of the number of moles n_{γ} will be

$$\frac{dn_{\gamma}}{dt} = \nu_{\gamma} \mathrm{v} \tag{1.4'}$$

Equations (1.1) to (1.4) can be extended easily to r simultaneous reactions. We shall always designate the different reactions by indices ρ ($\rho = 1 \ldots\ldots r$). The total change of mass dm_{γ} is then equal to the sum of the changes resulting from the different reactions

$$dm_{\gamma} = M_{\gamma} \sum_{\rho=1}^{r} \nu_{\gamma\rho} d\xi_{\rho} \tag{1.5}$$

or, for the number of moles

$$dn_{\gamma} = \sum_{\rho=1}^{r} \nu_{\gamma\rho} d\xi_{\rho} \tag{1.6}$$

where $\nu_{\gamma\rho}$ denotes the stoichiometric coefficient of γ in the reaction. The rate of the ρth reaction is clearly

$$v_\rho = \frac{d\xi_\rho}{dt} \tag{1.7}$$

As an example we may consider the two simultaneous reactions

$$\begin{aligned} 2C + O_2 &\rightarrow 2CO \qquad (\rho = 1) \\ C + O_2 &\rightarrow CO_2 \qquad (\rho = 2) \end{aligned}$$

We have

$$\begin{aligned} dn_{C} &= -2d\xi_1 - d\xi_2 \\ dn_{C_2} &= -d\xi_1 - d\xi_2 \\ dn_{CO_2} &= 2d\xi_1 \\ dn_{CO_2} &= d\xi_2 \end{aligned}$$

Equations (1.1) to (1.7) apply equally well to simple phase changes which may be treated as chemical reactions. Thus the solidification of water may be represented by the reaction

$$H_2O \text{ (liquid)} \rightarrow H_2O \text{ (solid)}$$

Although we have defined the degree of advancement only for chemical reactions with well-defined stoichiometric coefficients, more general physico-chemical transformations can also be characterized by such a parameter. For instance, the order-disorder transformation which is observed in an equimolecular Au-Cu alloy with increasing temperature, can still be characterized by an *internal parameter* related to the mean number of Cu atoms surrounding an Au atom. In these cases however no "chemical" equations with stoichiometric coefficients can be written down.

4. Conservation of Mass in Open Systems

In an open system we may split the change of mass of component γ into an external part $d_e m_\gamma$ supplied from the exterior, and an internal part $d_i m_\gamma$ due to changes inside the system.

$$dm_\gamma = d_e m_\gamma + d_i m_\gamma \tag{1.8}$$

Taking into account (1.5)

$$dm_\gamma = d_e m_\gamma + M_\gamma \sum_{\rho=1}^{r} \nu_{\gamma\rho} d\xi_\rho$$

or

$$dn_\gamma = d_e n_\gamma + \sum_{\rho=1}^{r} \nu_{\gamma\rho} d\xi_\rho \tag{1.8'}$$

Summing (1.8) over γ and taking into account the stoichiometric equations $\sum_\gamma \nu_{\gamma\rho} M_\gamma = 0$, we obtain for the total change of mass

$$dm = d_e m \tag{1.9}$$

This relation expresses the principle of conservation of mass in open systems and indicates that the change in the total mass is equal to the mass exchanged with the exterior. The process of splitting the total change of mass of component γ, dm_γ, into an external part, due to exchanges with the exterior, and an internal part resulting from reactions inside the system, may be generalized to any extensive property. For example, the formulation of the second principle of thermodynamics, introduced in Chapter III, is based on such a splitting of the total entropy change.

CHAPTER II

Conservation of Energy in Closed and Open Systems—The First Principle of Thermodynamics

1. Functions of the State

The thermodynamic state of a system may be defined by means of a certain number of independent variables like V, p and the number of moles $n_1 \ldots n_c$. Any function which may be expressed in terms of these variables is called a function of the state of the system. As an example, we may consider the refractive index which may be expressed in terms of the composition, the volume and the pressure and is thus a function of the state.

2. Conservation of Energy—The First Principle of Thermodynamics

The principle of conservation of energy will be introduced with a minimum of details. In its general form, this principle postulates the existence of a function of state, called the energy of the system, such that its change per unit time is equal to some flow called the energy flow from the surroundings.* This statement can be ex-

* More precisely, the change of energy per unit time must be equal to a surface integral extended over the boundaries of the system. The argument of this integral is the scalar product of the unit vector normal to the surface and the energy flow. A very thorough discussion of the first prin-

(*Continued*) →

pressed symbolically by a formula, analogous to (1.9)

$$dE = d_eE \qquad \text{or} \qquad d_iE = 0 \tag{2.1}$$

In a closed system and in the absence of an external field (cf., Chapter III, § 9) the energy supplied by the exterior during the time interval dt is equal to the sum of the heat dQ and the mechanical work $d\mathbf{T}$, performed at the boundaries of the system. dQ is counted positive if received by the system. If the pressure is normal to the surface, the mechanical work is simply $-p\,dV$ and (2.1) takes the usual form

$$dE = dQ - p\,dV \tag{2.2}$$

The differential sign d refers to an infinitesimally small change which occurs during the time interval dt.

Consider a system which undergoes an internal change, characterized by the parameter ξ. E is a function of the state and can be expressed as a function of independent variables: the volume V, the temperature T† and the number of moles $n_1 \ldots n_c$. In a closed system the number of moles may themselves be expressed in terms of the extent of reaction ξ (cf., 1.3). The total differential of E in the variables V, T, ξ can therefore be written

$$dE = \left(\frac{\partial E}{\partial V}\right)_{T\xi} dV + \left(\frac{\partial E}{\partial T}\right)_{V\xi} dT + \left(\frac{\partial E}{\partial \xi}\right)_{TV} d\xi \tag{2.3}$$

We may use this formula to obtain an expression for dQ in terms of the changes of the independent variables dT, dV, $d\xi$ during the time interval dt. Taking into account (2.2), we have

---

(*Continued from preceding page*)

ciple is found in Duhem's book, *Energetique* (Vol. I) [6]. Bridgman's book *The Nature of Thermodynamics* also contains many interesting considerations [7]. For the definition of heat in thermodynamics cf. M. Born [8].

† The absolute temperature will be defined in Chapter III. In this chapter T should be considered as an empirical temperature recorded by measuring the change of an arbitrary property, such as electrical resistance.

$$dQ = C_{V\xi} dT + l_{T\xi}\, dV - r_{TV} d\xi \tag{2.4}$$

with

$$\left(\frac{\partial E}{\partial T}\right)_{V\xi} = C_{V\xi}, \quad \left(\frac{\partial E}{\partial V}\right)_{T\xi} = l_{T\xi} - p, \quad \left(\frac{\partial E}{\partial \xi}\right)_{VT} = -r_{TV} \tag{2.5}$$

$C_{V\xi}$ is the heat capacity at constant volume for a given value of ξ, $l_{T\xi}$ gives the heat effect of compression at constant T and ξ (for a mixture of perfect gases $\frac{\partial E}{\partial V} = 0$, $l_{T\xi} = p$), and r_{VT} denotes the heat of reaction associated with a change of ξ at constant T and V (r_{TV} is positive for an exothermic reaction). The heat received dQ during the time interval dt may be calculated by means of (2.4). It should be noted that (2.4) is not a total differential in terms of the variables T, V, ξ like (2.3).

3. Enthalpy

We now introduce another function of state, the enthalpy H, defined by

$$H = E + pV \tag{2.6}$$

In terms of this function, the principle of conservation of energy may be written as

$$dH = dQ + V\, dp \tag{2.7}$$

Developing dH as a total differential in terms of the variables p, T, ξ we obtain instead of (2.4)

$$dQ = C_{p\xi} dT + h_{T\xi} dp - r_{Tp} d\xi \tag{2.8}$$

with

$$\left(\frac{\partial H}{\partial T}\right)_{p\xi} = C_{p\xi}; \quad \left(\frac{\partial H}{\partial p}\right)_{T\xi} = h_{T\xi} + V; \quad \left(\frac{\partial H}{\partial \xi}\right)_{Tp} = -r_{Tp} \tag{2.9}$$

These coefficients have a meaning analogous to that of the coefficients which appeared in (2.4). Using the variables p, T and $n_1 \ldots n_c$, dQ becomes

$$dQ = C_{p,\, n_1 \ldots n_c}\, dT + l_{T,\, n_1 \ldots n_c}\, dp + \sum_\gamma h_\gamma\, dn_\gamma \quad (2.10)$$

In this formula, h_γ is the specific enthalpy (per mole) of component γ

$$h_\gamma = \left(\frac{\partial H}{\partial n_\gamma}\right)_{pTn'_\gamma} \quad (2.11)$$

where n'_γ denotes all the mole numbers $n_1 \ldots n_c$ with the exception of n_γ.

Further on we shall also use the specific enthalpy of component *per unit mass*

$$h^+_\gamma = \left(\frac{\partial H}{\partial m_\gamma}\right)_{Tpm'_\gamma} = \frac{1}{M_\gamma} h_\gamma \quad (2.12)$$

Throughout this book the cross will always denote a reduction per unit mass.

We shall not go into further details regarding closed systems [cf., 9a].

4. Open Systems

When applying, to an open system, formula (2.2) which expresses conservation of energy, we must take into account the exchange of matter with the exterior. Instead of (2.2) we shall now write

$$dE = d\Phi - p\, dV \quad (2.13)$$

This formula is of the general form (2.1). Instead of the simple heat transfer dQ of (2.2) we now have a resultant flow of energy $d\Phi$ during the time interval dt, due to heat transfer and exchange of matter. Later on we shall calculate the actual value of $d\Phi$ for some special cases (cf., Chapter V). For the enthalpy we may write

$$dH = d\Phi + V\,dp \tag{2.14}$$

It is currently stated that energy or enthalpy is completely defined, apart from an arbitrary additive constant. Hence, instead of H, we may also write

$$H' = H + \alpha \tag{2.15}$$

where α is the additive constant. However, for a homogeneous system the extensive variable H is proportional to the mass of the system and of course the same is true for H'.

Thus α is also proportional to m and is no longer a constant for open systems and we can write

$$H' = H + \beta m \qquad \text{or} \qquad h^{+\prime} = h^{+} + \beta \tag{2.16}$$

where β is now a "real" constant. It immediately results from (2.16) that the change of enthalpy or energy in an open system is defined apart from the term βdm and this applies to $d\Phi$ also.

5. Examples

We consider a system formed by two phases (I and II). The system as a whole is closed, although each phase exchanges matter with the other and is therefore an open system in itself. Applying (2.14) to each phase we obtain

$$dH^{\mathrm{I}} = d^{\mathrm{I}}\Phi + V^{\mathrm{I}}dp^{\mathrm{I}}, \qquad dH^{\mathrm{II}} = d^{\mathrm{II}}\Phi + V^{\mathrm{II}}dp^{\mathrm{II}} \tag{2.17}$$

We have written $d^{\mathrm{I}}\Phi$ and not $d\Phi^{\mathrm{I}}$ because obviously $d\Phi$ is not a total differential. $d^{\mathrm{I}}\Phi$ represents the resultant flow of energy received by phase I during the time interval dt.

Assuming $p^{\mathrm{I}} = p^{\mathrm{II}} = p$, we can deduce from (2.17) the change of the total enthalpy

$$dH = d^{\mathrm{I}}\Phi + d^{\mathrm{II}}\Phi + V\,dp \tag{2.18}$$

where $V = V^{\mathrm{I}} + V^{\mathrm{II}}$.

As the system is closed, this equation must be identical with the usual formulation of the first principle (2.7)

$$dH = dQ + V\,dp \tag{2.19}$$

Hence

$$dQ = d^{\mathrm{I}}\Phi + d^{\mathrm{II}}\Phi \tag{2.20}$$

In order to understand the implications of this equation, let us observe that the resultant energy flow $d^{\mathrm{I}}\Phi$ received by phase I during the time interval dt, is equal to the ordinary heat coming from the exterior $d_e^{\mathrm{I}}Q$ plus the energy flow $d_i^{\mathrm{I}}\Phi$ from phase II:

$$d^{\mathrm{I}}\Phi = d_e^{\mathrm{I}}Q + d_i^{\mathrm{I}}\Phi \quad \text{and} \quad d^{\mathrm{II}}\Phi = d_e^{\mathrm{II}}Q + d_i^{\mathrm{II}}\Phi \tag{2.21}$$

Obviously

$$dQ = d_e^{\mathrm{I}}Q + d_e^{\mathrm{II}}Q \tag{2.22}$$

and using (2.20), we get

$$d_i^{\mathrm{I}}\Phi + d_i^{\mathrm{II}}\Phi = 0 \tag{2.23}$$

This relation expresses that the energy flow received by phase I from phase II is equal and of opposite sign to the energy flow received by phase II from phase I. For closed phases (2.23) reduces to the classical relationship

$$d_i^{\mathrm{I}}Q + d_i^{\mathrm{II}}Q = 0 \tag{2.24}$$

which expresses the conservation of energy for the system.

CHAPTER III

Entropy Production—The Second Principle of Thermodynamics

1. Reversible and Irreversible Processes

Let us consider equations which describe some time-dependent physical processes. If these equations are invariant with regard to the algebraic sign affixed to the variable time, the process is called a *reversible* process, otherwise it is called *irreversible.* In the equations describing reversible processes, time can appear only through its arithmetic value.

As an example, we may consider the wave equation which describes the propagation of waves in a non-absorbing medium

$$\frac{1}{c^2}\frac{\partial^2 u}{\partial t^2} = \frac{\partial^2 u}{\partial x^2} + \frac{\partial^2 u}{\partial y^2} + \frac{\partial^2 u}{\partial z^2} \tag{3.1}$$

Clearly, this equation is invariant for the substitution $t \to -t$ and the propagation described by this equation is therefore a reversible process.

On the other hand, the Fourier equation for temperature which is of the form

$$\frac{1}{\alpha}\frac{\partial T}{\partial t} = \frac{\partial^2 T}{\partial x^2} + \frac{\partial^2 T}{\partial y^2} + \frac{\partial^2 T}{\partial z^2} \tag{3.2}$$

is not invariant with respect to such a substitution and it describes an irreversible process: the irreversible approach to thermal equilibrium. In this equilibrium state, the temperature will be constant throughout the system provided the system is isolated.

Most of the usual physicochemical processes like diffusion, conduction of heat or electricity, chemical reactions, etc., are irreversible processes and the major progress in thermodynamics during the last twenty years is related to the extension of macroscopic methods to such processes. The importance of such a development results from the complexity of irreversible processes at a molecular scale which has thus far prevented the formulation of a statistical theory,* except in the case of gases.†

However, even when a detailed theory will become available, thermodynamics of irreversible processes will still be of considerable importance, comparable to the importance of thermodynamics of equilibria, by showing which results depend on special microscopic assumptions, for example, assumptions on molecular interactions, and which results are of general validity.

The second principle of thermodynamics will be introduced in two stages. The first, in section 2, is to introduce entropy by enumerating its basic properties but without calculation of its actual value. The second stage is reached in the subsequent sections and results in the formulation of explicit formulae for the entropy.

2. Entropy

The second principle of thermodynamics postulates the existence of a function of state, called entropy (from the Greek εν τρωπη meaning "evolution") which possesses the following properties:

* For some recent attempts, cf. Kirkwood [10], Born and Green [11] Klein and Prigogine [58].

† Cf. Chapman and Cowling [12].

a) The entropy of the system is an *extensive* property. If a system consists of several parts, therefore the total entropy is equal to the sum of the entropies of each part.

b) The change of entropy dS can be split into two parts. Denoting by d_eS the flow of entropy, due to interactions with the exterior, and by d_iS the contribution due to changes inside the system, we have

$$dS = d_eS + d_iS \tag{3.3}$$

The entropy increase d_iS, due to changes inside the system, is never negative. It is zero when the system undergoes reversible changes only, but it is positive if the system is subject to irreversible processes as well.

$$d_iS = 0 \quad \text{(reversible processes)} \tag{3.4}$$

$$d_iS > 0 \quad \text{(irreversible processes)} \tag{3.5}$$

In this chapter we shall calculate explicit expressions for the entropy production of some important irreversible processes and also the entropy flow related to exchanges of matter and of energy with the external environment. Before doing so it is convenient to add a few remarks at this stage.

For isolated systems, there is no flow of entropy so that (3.3) and (3.5) reduce to

$$dS = d_iS \geqslant 0 \quad \text{(isolated system)} \tag{3.6}$$

For isolated systems, this relation is equivalent to the classical statement that entropy can never decrease, so that in this case the behavior of the entropy function provides a criterion which enables us to detect the presence of irreversible processes. Similar criteria exist for some other particular cases. For instance, it is shown in textbooks on thermodynamics that for closed systems, at constant temperature and volume, the Helmholtz free energy $F = E - TS$ decreases when irreversible changes occur and remains constant otherwise. However, functions like S, F, exist only for a very limited number of transformations (for example, changes at constant temperature and volume or at constant temperature and pressure, as well as for some others). The only *general criterion* of irreversibility is given by the entropy production according to (3.4) and (3.5).

Suppose we enclose a system which we shall denote by I, inside a larger system II, so that the global system containing both I and II is isolated. In both parts, I and II, some irreversible process may take place. The classical statement of the second law of thermodynamics would be

$$dS = dS^{\mathrm{I}} + dS^{\mathrm{II}} \geqslant 0$$

Applying now (3.4)–(3.5) to each part separately, we shall postulate here that

$$d_iS^{\mathrm{I}} \geqslant 0, \qquad d_iS^{\mathrm{II}} \geqslant 0$$

A physical situation such that

$$d_iS^{\mathrm{I}} > 0, \qquad d_iS^{\mathrm{II}} < 0 \qquad \text{with } d(S^{\mathrm{I}} + S^{\mathrm{II}}) > 0$$

is excluded. We can therefore say that "absorption" of entropy in one part, compensated by a sufficient "production" in another part of the system is prohibited. This formulation implies that in every macroscopic region of the system the entropy production due to the irreversible processes is positive. The term macroscopic region refers to any region containing a number of molecules sufficiently large for microscopic fluctuations to be negligible. Interference of irreversible processes is only possible when they occur in the same region of the system. Such a formulation may be called a "*local*" formulation of the second law in contrast to the "*global*" formulation of classical thermodynamics. Its value lies in the fact that it permits a much closer analysis of irreversible processes and, as such, it will constitute the central postulate on which this book is based. This postulate will have to be justified eventually by considerations based on statistical mechanics [34].

It is interesting to note that the splitting of the entropy change into two terms d_iS and d_eS permits an easy discussion of the difference between closed and open systems as will be shown below. Clearly, this difference has to appear in the term d_eS which, for open systems, must contain terms due to the exchange of matter.

3. Entropy of One-component Systems—Absolute Temperature

We shall consider first a closed system containing a single component, an irreversible processes being excluded ($d_iS = 0$). We shall then define the entropy by the explicit formula

$$dS = \frac{dQ}{T} \tag{3.7}$$

where T is a positive quantity called *absolute temperature*, which satisfies the following requirements:

a) T is positive.

b) T is a universal function of the temperature of the system as recorded by measuring some arbitrary property like electrical resistance; T is an intensive property.

c) T is an increasing function of the "empirical" temperature of the system.

We shall show in the subsequent paragraphs that the quantity (3.7) has really the general properties enumerated in § 2.

It is clear that the formula (3.7) defining entropy and absolute temperature still remains valid when S is multiplied by some constant a and T by a^{-1}.* Thus to complete the definitions of S and T we have to assign an arbitrary value to T for a well-defined point in the empirical scale (the value $T = 273.16$ degrees at the equilibrium between liquid water and ice at a pressure of one atmosphere is now generally adopted as the reference temperature). We shall not go into details as regards scales of temperature.

We note that, by using (2.2),

$$dS = \frac{dE + pdV}{T} \tag{3.8}$$

In § 5 this formula will be generalized to many-component systems.

We shall now show that formula (3.7), when applied to the irreversible process of heat flow between systems at different temperatures, gives results which agree with the basic properties of the entropy as postulated in § 2.

4. Entropy Production Due to Heat Flow

We consider again a system consisting of two closed phases, I and II, maintained respectively at uniform temperature T^{I} and T^{II}. Applying formula (3.7) or (3.8) to each phase, we have for the whole system, entropy being an extensive variable,

$$dS = dS^{\text{I}} + dS^{\text{II}} \tag{3.9}$$

We now split the heat received by each phase into two parts (cf. 2.22)

$$d^{\text{I}}Q = d_i^{\text{I}}Q + d_e^{\text{I}}Q, \qquad d^{\text{II}}Q = d_i^{\text{II}}Q + d_e^{\text{II}}Q \tag{3.10}$$

where $d_i^{\text{I}}Q$ is the heat received by phase I from phase II and $d_e^{\text{II}}Q$ the heat supplied to phase I from the outside. Taking account of (2.24), we have for the entropy change

* For further details cf. Guggenheim [13], p. 12.

of the whole system

$$dS = \frac{d^{\mathrm{I}}Q}{T^{\mathrm{I}}} + \frac{d^{\mathrm{II}}Q}{T^{\mathrm{II}}} \tag{3.11}$$

$$= \frac{d_e^{\mathrm{I}}Q}{T^{\mathrm{I}}} + \frac{d_e^{\mathrm{II}}Q}{T^{\mathrm{II}}} + d_i^{\mathrm{I}}Q\left(\frac{1}{T^{\mathrm{I}}} - \frac{1}{T^{\mathrm{II}}}\right) \tag{3.12}$$

In agreement with (3.3) the entropy change consists of two parts. The first

$$d_eS = \frac{d_e^{\mathrm{I}}Q}{T^{\mathrm{I}}} + \frac{d_e^{\mathrm{II}}Q}{T^{\mathrm{II}}} \tag{3.13}$$

is due to the exchange of heat with the exterior, while the second part

$$d_iS = d_i^{\mathrm{I}}Q\left(\frac{1}{T^{\mathrm{I}}} - \frac{1}{T^{\mathrm{II}}}\right) \tag{3.14}$$

results from the irreversible heat flow inside the system. In agreement with (3.5) we may postulate that the entropy production is really positive. In fact

$$d_i^{\mathrm{I}}Q > 0 \qquad \text{when } \frac{1}{T^{\mathrm{I}}} - \frac{1}{T^{\mathrm{II}}} > 0$$

$$d_i^{\mathrm{I}}Q < 0 \qquad \text{when } \frac{1}{T^{\mathrm{I}}} - \frac{1}{T^{\mathrm{II}}} < 0$$

The entropy production can only be zero when thermal equilibrium is established, that is when

$$T^{\mathrm{I}} = T^{\mathrm{II}} \tag{3.15}$$

Further on, we shall often make use of the entropy production per unit time

$$\frac{d_iS}{dt} = \frac{d_i^{\mathrm{I}}Q}{dt}\left(\frac{1}{T^{\mathrm{I}}} - \frac{1}{T^{\mathrm{II}}}\right) > 0 \tag{3.16}$$

This equation is of a simple form which is of great importance. It is the product of the rate of the irreversible process ($d_i^{\text{I}}Q/dt$) by the function of state ($1/T^{\text{I}} - 1/T^{\text{II}}$). The direction of the heat flow is determined by the sign of this function, which can therefore be considered as its macroscopic "cause."

5. Entropy of Multicomponent Systems—Chemical Potentials

Formula (3.8) gives the total differential of the entropy as function of the variables E and V. We now have to generalize this formula by taking into account all possible changes in the mole numbers $n_1 \ldots n_c$.

Thus, instead of (3.8), we shall write the more general formula

$$dS = \frac{dE}{T} + \frac{p}{T}dV - \sum_{\gamma} \frac{\mu_\gamma}{T} dn_\gamma \qquad (3.17)$$

The quantities μ_γ are called *chemical potentials* and are defined by

$$\mu_\gamma = -T\left(\frac{\partial S}{\partial n_\gamma}\right)_{EVn_\gamma} \qquad (3.18)$$

where n'_γ denotes again (cf., 2.11) all the mole numbers $n_1 \ldots n_c$ with exception of n_γ. Like the other partial derivatives of S ($1/T = \partial S/\partial E$, $p/T = \partial S/\partial V$) the chemical potentials are intensive variables.

Formula (3.17) is due to Gibbs and plays a fundamental role in the evaluation of the entropy production as we shall see further on. In the next paragraph, it will also become apparent why the chemical potentials are of outstanding importance for the thermodynamics of physico-chemical equilibrium.

The chemical potentials can be expressed in a number of ways all equivalent to (3.18). First, considering (3.17) as the total differential of E in variables S, V, n_γ, we have

$$\mu_\gamma = \left(\frac{\partial E}{\partial n_\gamma}\right)_{SVn'_\gamma} \qquad (3.19)$$

Introducing the enthalpy $H = E + pV$, the Helmholtz free energy $F = E - TS$ or the Gibbs free energy $G = H - TS$, it can also be easily verified that

$$\mu_\gamma = \left(\frac{\partial H}{\partial n_\gamma}\right)_{Spn_\gamma'} = \left(\frac{\partial F}{\partial n_\gamma}\right)_{TVn_\gamma'} = \left(\frac{\partial G}{\partial n_\gamma}\right)_{Tpn_\gamma'} \tag{3.20}$$

Many other properties of the chemical potentials are indicated in textbooks of chemical thermodynamics. We note in passing, the following relations

$$\left(\frac{\partial \mu_\gamma}{\partial T}\right)_{pn\gamma} = -s_\gamma, \left(\frac{\partial \mu_\gamma}{\partial p}\right)_{Tn\gamma} = v_\gamma, \left(\frac{\partial(\mu_\gamma/T)}{\partial T}\right)_{pn\gamma} = -\frac{h_\gamma}{T^2} \tag{3.21}$$

where s_γ, v_γ and h_γ are respectively the specific molar entropy, volume and enthalpy of component γ as defined by

$$s_\gamma = \left(\frac{\partial S}{\partial n_\gamma}\right)_{pTn_\gamma'}, v_\gamma = \left(\frac{\partial V}{\partial n_\gamma}\right)_{Tpn_\gamma'}, h_\gamma = \left(\frac{\partial H}{\partial n_\gamma}\right)_{pTn_\gamma'} \tag{3.22}$$

For many systems known as "*ideal systems*" (mixtures of perfect gases, socalled "perfect solutions" formed by components of nearly similar molecules like isotopes, very dilute solutions etc.) the chemical potentials take the form

$$\mu_\gamma = \zeta_\gamma\ (p, T) + RT \log N_\gamma \tag{3.23}$$

where $\zeta_\gamma\ (p, T)$ is independent of composition while N_γ denotes the mole fraction ($= n_\gamma/n$). Different ideal systems may differ with respect to the value of the functions $\zeta_\gamma(p, T)$. For perfect gases the pressure dependence of $\zeta_\gamma\ (p, T)$ is of the form

$$\zeta_\gamma(p, T) = RT \log p + \eta_\gamma(T) \tag{3.24}$$

where $\eta_\gamma\ (T)$ is independent of both composition and pressure. For non-ideal systems it is customary to preserve, as far as possible, the form (3.21) and to write

$$\mu_\gamma = \zeta_\gamma(p, T) + RT \log f_\gamma N_\gamma \qquad (3.25)$$

where f_γ is the *activity coefficient*, due to G. N. Lewis.

6. Entropy Production Due to Chemical Reactions—Affinity—Coupling of Chemical Reactions

From (3.17) we shall deduce an expression for the entropy flow and entropy production originated by chemical reactions in closed systems. Taking into account (1.3) and (2.2), we get

$$dS = \frac{dQ}{T} + \frac{A d\xi}{T} \qquad (3.26)$$

where A is the *affinity* of the chemical reaction related to the chemical potentials by

$$A = -\sum_\gamma \nu_\gamma \mu_\gamma \qquad (3.27)$$

This definition of affinity is due to Th. De Donder [2–7, 9].

The entropy change is composed again of two terms:

1) The entropy change due to interactions with the exterior

$$d_e S = \frac{dQ}{T} \qquad (3.28)$$

For the closed system studied here this term is, of course, identical with (3.7).

2) The entropy production

$$d_i S = \frac{A d\xi}{T} > 0 \qquad (3.29)$$

For the equilibrium state

$$A = -\sum_\gamma \nu_\gamma \mu_\gamma = 0 \qquad (3.30)$$

In particular, if the transformation consists in the passage of the component γ from phase I to phase II, the equilibrium condition (3.30) becomes simply

$$\mu_\gamma^{\mathrm{I}} = \mu_\gamma^{\mathrm{II}} \tag{3.31}$$

Relations (3.30) and (3.31) clearly show why the chemical potentials play such an important role in the thermodynamics of equilibria. The affinity is also closely related to the chemical reaction rate v since we have for the entropy production per unit time (cf., 1.4)

$$\frac{d_iS}{dt} = \frac{1}{T} A\mathrm{v} > 0 \tag{3.32}$$

A and v have always the same sign and this circumstance justifies the term "affinity" given by De Donder to the function A. It will be noted that this relation is similar to (3.16), the role of $(1/T^{\mathrm{I}} - 1/T^{\mathrm{II}})$ having been taken over here by the affinity. The inequality (3.32), due to De Donder, expresses the most characteristic property of the chemical affinity. It should be emphasized too that the main interest of De Donder's definition of chemical affinity resides in the fact that affinity, so defined, is closely related to entropy production.

The preceding formulae are readily extended to the case of several simultaneous reactions. Instead of (3.32) we then get

$$d_iS = \frac{1}{T} \sum_\rho A_\rho d\xi_\rho > 0 \tag{3.33}$$

where A_ρ is the affinity of the ρth reaction related to the chemical potentials by

$$A_\rho = - \sum_\gamma \nu_{\gamma\rho}\mu_\gamma \tag{3.34}$$

In the equilibrium state, all affinities are zero

$$A_1 = A_2 = \ldots = A_r = 0 \tag{3.35}$$

The entropy production per unit time is now

$$\frac{d_iS}{dt} = \frac{1}{T}\sum_\rho A_\rho v_\rho > 0 \tag{3.36}$$

This is a bilinear form of the affinities and rates of chemical reactions. We shall again encounter this form when we study other irreversible processes. Let us notice also that the entropy production per unit time is the sum of the entropy production due to the various reactions.

The second principle requires that the entropy production resulting from all the simultaneous reactions is positive. However, it may happen that a system undergoes two simultaneous reactions such that

$$A_1 v_1 < 0, \qquad A_2 v_2 > 0 \tag{3.37}$$

provided that the sum

$$A_1 v_1 + A_2 v_2 > 0 \tag{3.38}$$

Both reactions are then called "*coupled*" reactions. Thermodynamic coupling allows one of the reactions to progress in a direction contrary to that prescribed by its own affinity. Such a coupling of irreversible processes will be studied more closely in the next chapter. For example, in thermodiffusion, the diffusion of matter against its concentration gradient is accompanied by a negative entropy production but this effect is compensated by the positive entropy production due to the flow of heat.

It is well known that coupled reactions are of great importance in biological processes. It has been verified experimentally that total entropy production is positive (cf., [14]).

7. Chemical Affinity

In order to become better acquainted with the physical meaning of the chemical affinity, we shall derive some explicit formulae which relate the affinity to the law of mass action, to the Gibbs free energy G, and to the heat of reaction (for further details, cf. [9a]).

Using (3.25) and (3.27) we obtain for an ideal system, ($f_\gamma = 1$),

$$A = -\sum_\gamma \nu_\gamma \zeta_\gamma(p, T) - RT \sum_\gamma \nu_\gamma \log N_\gamma \tag{3.39}$$

Introducing the equilibrium constant $K(T, p)$, defined by

$$RT \log K(p, T) = -\sum_\gamma \nu_\gamma \zeta_\gamma(p, T) \tag{3.40}$$

we can write the affinity in the form

$$A = RT \log \frac{K(p, T)}{N_1^{\nu_1} \dots N_c^{\nu_c}} \tag{3.41}$$

The state of equilibrium is defined by $A = 0$, whence

$$K(p, T) = N_1^{\nu_1} \dots N_c^{\nu_c} \tag{3.42}$$

This is the familiar form of the law of mass action. For non-ideal systems this law has to be corrected by introducing activity coefficients according to (3.25). An alternative expression for the affinity may be obtained by using the third of relations (3.20), so that

$$A = -\sum \nu_\gamma \left(\frac{\partial G}{\partial n_\gamma}\right)_{P,\, T\, n'_\gamma} \tag{3.43}$$

Using (1.3), it follows that

$$\left(\frac{\partial G}{\partial \xi}\right)_{pT} = \sum_\gamma \left(\frac{\partial G}{\partial n_\gamma}\right)_{pT} \frac{dn_\gamma}{d\xi} = \sum_\gamma \left(\frac{\partial G}{\partial n_\gamma}\right)_{pT} \nu_\gamma$$

The affinity may therefore be written as

$$A = -\left(\frac{\partial G}{\partial \xi}\right)_{pT} \tag{3.44}$$

which expresses the affinity as a partial derivative of the

Gibbs free energy. Using the expression for the Gibbs free energy $G = H - TS$ and (2.9), we also obtain a direct relation between affinity and heat of reaction.

$$A = -\left(\frac{\partial H}{\partial \xi}\right)_{pT} + T\left(\frac{\partial S}{\partial \xi}\right)_{pT} = r_{pT} + T\left(\frac{\partial S}{\partial \xi}\right)_{pT} \tag{3.45}$$

In textbooks on classical thermodynamics it is shown that it is sometimes possible to neglect the entropy variation term in (3.45). In such cases the entropy production due to a chemical change becomes simply proportional to the heat of reaction (cf., 2.8)

$$\frac{d_iS}{dt} = \frac{A\mathrm{v}}{T} \approx \frac{r_{pT}\mathrm{v}}{T} = -\frac{1}{T}\left(\frac{dQ}{dt}\right)_{pT} \tag{3.46}$$

For simultaneous reactions, where $r_{pT}^{(\rho)}$ is the heat of the reaction ρ

$$\frac{d_iS}{dt} \approx \frac{1}{T}\sum_{\rho} r_{pT}^{(\rho)}\,\mathrm{v}_{\rho} = -\frac{1}{T}\left(\frac{dQ}{dt}\right)_{pT} \tag{3.46'}$$

In this approximation the entropy production of a living organism can be measured by its metabolism, as recorded by calorimetry. In this approximation also, a coupled reaction ($A\mathrm{v} < 0$) is equivalent to an endothermic reaction ($r_{pT}\mathrm{v} < 0$) and the presence of such coupled reactions will then manifest itself by a diminution of the total heat which the system gives off to the external world. Many authors have tried to determine experimentally such a diminution of the heat effect during the embryonic period [15] when, because of organization processes, coupled reactions must presumably play a particularly important role. Such heat effects should be interpreted with great care as the condition $|r_{pT}| \gg T\left|\left(\frac{\partial S}{\partial \xi}\right)_{pT}\right|$ is in many cases a poor approximation.

8. Entropy Production and Entropy Flow in Open Systems

By following closely the same argument as in § 6, we shall calculate the entropy flow in open systems. The starting point will again be Gibbs formula (3.17) but we now have to combine it with (1.8) and (2.13). Instead of (3.26) we get

$$dS = \frac{d\Phi}{T} - \sum_{\gamma} \frac{\mu_\gamma}{T}\, d_e n_\gamma + \frac{A\,d\xi}{T} \tag{3.47}$$

As might be expected, only the term due to the exchange of entropy with the surroundings is modified

$$d_e S = \frac{d\Phi}{T} - \sum_{\gamma} \frac{\mu_\gamma}{T}\, d_e n_\gamma \tag{3.48}$$

We shall now apply (3.47) to the system already considered in Chapter II, § 4. This system consists of two open phases but is closed as a whole; moreover, we shall suppose that each phase has a well-defined temperature. Summing (3.47) for both phases, the change of the total entropy of the system is expressed by

$$dS = \frac{d^{\mathrm{I}}\Phi}{T^{\mathrm{I}}} + \frac{d^{\mathrm{II}}\Phi}{T^{\mathrm{II}}} - \sum_{\gamma}\left(\frac{\mu_\gamma^{\mathrm{I}}}{T^{\mathrm{I}}} - \frac{\mu_\gamma^{\mathrm{II}}}{T^{\mathrm{II}}}\right) d_e n_\gamma^{\mathrm{I}} + \frac{A^{\mathrm{I}}d\xi^{\mathrm{I}}}{T^{\mathrm{I}}} + \frac{A^{\mathrm{II}}d\xi^{\mathrm{II}}}{T^{\mathrm{II}}} \tag{3.49}$$

where A^{I} and A^{II} are the affinities of reactions taking place in each phase. Making use of the splitting (2.21), we may write (3.49) in the form

$$dS = \frac{d_e^{\mathrm{I}}Q}{T^{\mathrm{I}}} + \frac{d_e^{\mathrm{II}}Q}{T^{\mathrm{II}}} + d_i^{\mathrm{I}}\Phi\left(\frac{1}{T^{\mathrm{I}}} - \frac{1}{T^{\mathrm{II}}}\right) - \sum_{\gamma}\left(\frac{\mu_\gamma^{\mathrm{I}}}{T^{\mathrm{I}}} - \frac{\mu_\gamma^{\mathrm{II}}}{T^{\mathrm{II}}}\right) d_e n_\gamma^{\mathrm{I}} + \frac{A^{\mathrm{I}}d\xi^{\mathrm{I}}}{T^{\mathrm{I}}} + \frac{A^{\mathrm{II}}d\xi^{\mathrm{II}}}{T^{\mathrm{II}}} \tag{3.50}$$

Clearly this change corresponds to the entropy flow

$$d_eS = \frac{d_e^{\mathrm{I}}Q}{T^{\mathrm{I}}} + \frac{d_e^{\mathrm{II}}Q}{T^{\mathrm{II}}} \tag{3.51}$$

and to an entropy production

$$d_iS = \left(\frac{1}{T^{\mathrm{I}}} - \frac{1}{T^{\mathrm{II}}}\right) d_i^{\mathrm{I}}\Phi - \sum_\gamma \left(\frac{\mu_\gamma^{\mathrm{I}}}{T^{\mathrm{I}}} - \frac{\mu_\gamma^{\mathrm{II}}}{T^{\mathrm{II}}}\right) d_e n_\gamma^{\mathrm{I}} + \frac{A^{\mathrm{I}} d\xi^{\mathrm{I}}}{T^{\mathrm{I}}} + \frac{A^{\mathrm{II}} d\xi^{\mathrm{II}}}{T^{\mathrm{II}}} > 0 \tag{3.52}$$

This entropy production results from a transport of heat and matter between the two phases of the system and also from the chemical reaction taking place in each phase. We shall examine some applications of this important formula in the next chapter. Attention may be drawn again to the simple form of the entropy production per unit time

$$\frac{d_iS}{dt} = \left(\frac{1}{T^{\mathrm{I}}} - \frac{1}{T^{\mathrm{II}}}\right) \frac{d_i^{\mathrm{I}}\Phi}{dt} - \sum_\gamma \left(\frac{\mu_\gamma^{\mathrm{I}}}{T^{\mathrm{I}}} - \frac{\mu_\gamma^{\mathrm{II}}}{T^{\mathrm{II}}}\right) \frac{d_e n_\gamma^{\mathrm{I}}}{dt} + \frac{A^{\mathrm{I}} \mathrm{v}^{\mathrm{I}}}{T^{\mathrm{I}}} + \frac{A^{\mathrm{II}} \mathrm{v}^{\mathrm{II}}}{T^{\mathrm{II}}} \geqslant 0 \tag{3.53}$$

Again we find that the entropy production is a bilinear form of the rates of the irreversible processes and of some functions of state which may be called "affinities" or "generalized forces."

Let us note the difference in the entropy flow as expressed by the two formulae (3.48) and (3.51). In the second case, the system as a whole is closed and therefore no terms due to exchanges of matter appear. Exchange of matter inside the system now appears in the entropy production (3.53).

9. Entropy Production Due to Electrochemical Reactions

The methods of the preceding sections can easily be generalized so as to include such cases as electrochemical or photochemical reactions. The only additional requirement is that account should be taken of the presence of an electrical or radiation field in equations (2.1) or (2.2) which express conservation of energy.

We shall now study a definite example: the transport of some electrically charged components from a position where the electrical potential is φ^{I} to a position with potential φ^{II}. For convenience we shall imagine that our system consists of two parts, each at a well-defined electrical potential, while the system as a whole is closed. Introducing the degree of advancement of the phase change, we have

$$-dn_\gamma^{\mathrm{I}} = dn_\gamma^{\mathrm{II}} = d\xi_\gamma \tag{3.54}$$

We shall denote by z_γ the electrovalency of the ionic component which is being transported, and by $\mathfrak{F}$ the Faraday, that is, the electrical charge associated with one gram-ion of a species having an electrovalency 1 ($\mathfrak{F} = 0{,}9649.10^5$ coulombs). The intensity of the electrical current is then related to the degree of advancement ξ_γ and to the rate of the phase change by the following relation

$$I = z_\gamma\, \mathfrak{F} \frac{d\xi_\gamma}{dt} = z_\gamma\, \mathfrak{F}_\gamma \tag{3.55}$$

The energy equation (2.2) now contains an additional term expressing the change of electrical energy into internal energy

$$dE = dQ - p\, dV + (\varphi^{\mathrm{I}} - \varphi^{\mathrm{II}})\, \mathrm{I}\, dt \tag{3.56}$$

We shall assume that the Gibbs equation (3.17) is still valid. This is equivalent to the assumption that the entropy can be completely expressed as a function of the energy, volume and composition, even in the presence of an electrical field. Such an hypothesis is in agreement with the statistical treatment of entropy in an electrical field as long as possible variations of the polarization of matter are not taken into account. Polarization is mainly associated with orientation of molecules, and orientation of molecules in an electrical field is followed by a decrease of entropy.*

For our two-phase system, the Gibbs equation can be written as

$$dS = \frac{1}{T}\,dE + \frac{p}{T}\,dV - \sum_{\gamma}\left(\frac{\mu_{\gamma}^{\mathrm{I}}}{T}\,dn_{\gamma}^{\mathrm{I}} + \frac{\mu_{\gamma}^{\mathrm{II}}}{T}\,dn_{\gamma}^{\mathrm{II}}\right) \qquad (3.57)$$

if it is assumed that the temperature is uniform throughout the whole system. We find the entropy balance by inserting (3.54)–(3.56) into (3.57)

$$dS = \frac{dQ}{T} + \frac{\tilde{A}_{\gamma}d\xi_{\gamma}}{T} \qquad (3.58)$$

with the notation

$$\tilde{A}_{\gamma} = A_{\gamma} + z_{\gamma}\mathfrak{F}(\varphi^{\mathrm{I}} - \varphi^{\mathrm{II}}) = (\mu_{\gamma}^{\mathrm{I}} + z_{\gamma}\mathfrak{F}\varphi^{\mathrm{I}}) - (\mu_{\gamma}^{\mathrm{II}} + z_{\gamma}^{\mathrm{II}}\,\mathfrak{F}\varphi) \qquad (3.59)$$

$\tilde{A}_{\gamma}$ is the electrochemical affinity corresponding to the transfer of the component γ from phase I to phase II. The expression

$$\tilde{\mu}_{\gamma} = \mu_{\gamma} + z_{\gamma}\mathfrak{F}\varphi \qquad (3.60)$$

is called the electrochemical potential [13]. It consists of the ordinary chemical contribution μ_{γ} and the electrical part $z_{\gamma}\mathfrak{F}\varphi$ (for details concerning the separate measurability of both parts see de Groot and Tolhoek [16]). The entropy production corresponding to (3.58) is given by

$$d_{i}S = \frac{\tilde{A}_{\gamma}d\xi_{\gamma}}{T} \qquad (3.61)$$

* The general case has been studied recently by the author, P. Mazur and R. Defay [59].

This rather remarkable result expresses the entropy production due to a single irreversible process and follows from the connection (3.55) between current and reaction rate. The presence of the electrical potentials thus manifests itself only by altering the value of the affinity. At equilibrium

$$\tilde{A}_\gamma = 0 \qquad \text{or} \qquad \mu_\gamma^{\mathrm{I}} - \mu_\gamma^{\mathrm{II}} = -z_\gamma \mathfrak{F}(\varphi^{\mathrm{I}} - \varphi^{\mathrm{II}}) \quad (3.62)$$

The classical equilibrium electrochemistry follows entirely from (3.62) [13, 17, 18].

10. Entropy Production in Continuous Systems

So far, we have only considered systems which consist of a finite number of homogeneous regions. The intensive state variables have the same value throughout each homogeneous region but they have different values in different regions. As a result the intensive properties are discontinuous at the boundary of the homogeneous regions and we may call such systems "*discontinuous systems.*" In this section, we shall briefly study systems in which the intensive state variables are not only functions of time but also continuous functions of the space coordinates. These systems may be called *continuous* systems. A piece of metal heated at one end and cooled at the other, or a mixture of diffusing components can be considered as examples of continuous systems.

The extension of our results to continuous systems involves no new physical principles. However, the full description of such systems requires a rather intricate mathematical formalism which is beyond the scope of this book. We shall therefore limit ourselves to quoting some important results. Full developments may be found elsewhere [9c, 17, 18].

The conservation of mass in a continuous system is expressed by the so-called equation of continuity for the density ρ

$$\frac{\partial \rho}{\partial t} = -\operatorname{div} \rho \omega \tag{3.63}$$

where ω is the macroscopic velocity. Equation (3.63) expresses that the local change of the density (left-hand member) is equal to the negative divergence of the flow of matter $\rho\omega$. In rectangular coordinates, the explicit expression of the divergence is

$$\operatorname{div} \rho\omega = \frac{\partial \rho\omega_x}{\partial x} + \frac{\partial \rho\omega_y}{\partial y} + \frac{\partial \rho\omega_z}{\partial z} \tag{3.64}$$

The divergence of a flow has the simple physical meaning of giving, per unit volume, the excess of the flow which leaves a small volume to the flow which penetrates into it.

Equation (3.63) holds equally well for a mixture; ω is then related to the macroscopic velocities of the different constituents by

$$\omega = \left(\sum_\gamma \rho_\gamma \omega_\gamma\right)/\rho \tag{3.65}$$

Thus ω is simply the velocity of the center of gravity in an element of volume.

In general, the local change of a physical quantity is due not only to the divergence of the current which is associated with it but a "*source*" term has also to be taken into account. For instance, the equation of continuity for the density ρ_γ of a component γ participating in a chemical reaction is given by (cf., 1.1 and 1.4)

$$\frac{\partial \rho_\gamma}{\partial t} = -\operatorname{div} \rho_\gamma \omega + \nu_\gamma M_\gamma \mathrm{v}_v \tag{3.66}$$

where v_v is the rate of the chemical reaction per *unit volume*. The flow of component γ can be decomposed into a flow with the average mass velocity ω (3.65) and a diffusion flow relative to ω

$$\rho_\gamma \omega_\gamma = \rho_\gamma \omega + \rho_\gamma(\omega_\gamma - \omega) = \rho_\gamma \omega + \rho_\gamma \Delta_\gamma \qquad (3.67)$$

where Δ_γ denotes the diffusion velocity with respect to ω. We may note that

$$\sum \rho_\gamma \Delta_\gamma = 0 \qquad (3.68)$$

An equation similar to (3.66) can be established for every variable having the properties of a generalized "*density*" like ρ or ρ_γ, i.e., an extensive variable per unit volume. Thus for the entropy per unit volume, s_v, we may write the equation of continuity

$$\frac{\partial s_v}{\partial t} = - \operatorname{div} \mathbf{\Phi} + \sigma \qquad (3.69)$$

where $\mathbf{\Phi}$ is the flow of entropy and σ the entropy production per unit volume and unit time. This equation is the extension of (3.3) to continuous systems. Instead of (3.4) and (3.5) we now postulate that

$$\sigma = 0 \quad \text{(reversible processes)} \qquad (3.70)$$

$$\sigma > 0 \quad \text{(irreversible processes)} \qquad (3.71)$$

The actual calculation of the local entropy production proceeds on exactly the same lines as for discontinuous systems and is based on the Gibbs equation (3.17). As the calculations are rather lengthy we shall only quote the results for a system in which thermal conduction, diffusion and chemical reactions are taking place. It is found that

$$\sigma = - \sum_i \frac{W^i}{T^2}\frac{\partial T}{\partial x^i} + \sum_\gamma \sum_i \frac{1}{T}\left(\mathfrak{F}_\gamma^i - T\frac{\partial \mu_\gamma^+/T}{\partial x^i}\right)\rho_\gamma \Delta_\gamma^i + \frac{A\mathrm{v}_v}{T} > 0 \qquad (3.72)$$

where $\mathfrak{F}_\gamma$ is the force (per unit mass) acting on the component γ. The summation over γ in (3.72) refers as usual to a summation over all components ($\gamma = 1 \ldots c$); the summation over i ($i = 1, 2, 3$) refers to the *geometrical coordinates* ($x^1 \equiv x, x^2 \equiv y, x^3 \equiv z$).

This formula is analogous to (3.53). It must be borne in mind however that in (3.53) the entropy production is due to the exchange of all the c constituents between the two phases and in fact, all the c quantities $d_e n_\gamma / dt$ appear in (3.53). In the present description of continuous systems we have to distinguish between the bulk movement with velocity ω (3.65) and the c diffusion flows $\rho_\gamma \ \Delta_\gamma$ (3.67) out of which only $(c - 1)$ are linearly independent (cf., 3.68). For non-viscous systems the velocity of the center of gravity does not appear in the source (3.72) and is therefore to be considered as a reversible phenomenon. The irreversibility is only related to diffusion and it is clear that, in a two-component system, in the absence of a temperature gradient or a chemical reaction, we shall have only one independent irreversible process. In a two-component system, without temperature gradient and chemical reaction, (3.72) reduces to

$$\sigma = \frac{1}{T}\left(\mathfrak{F}_1 - \frac{\partial \mu_1^+}{\partial x}\right) \rho_1 \Delta_1 + \frac{1}{T}\left(\mathfrak{F}_2 - \frac{\partial \mu_2^+}{\partial x}\right) \rho_2 \Delta_2 > 0 \quad (3.73)$$

where the diffusion flows are related by (3.68). For convenience, we assume here that the forces and concentration gradients act along the geometrical coordinate x only. For many systems it can be assumed that mechanical equilibrium is reached. It can then be shown (cf. [17, 18]) that

$$\rho_1 \left(\mathfrak{F}_1 - \frac{\partial \mu_1^+}{\partial x}\right) + \rho_2 \left(\mathfrak{F}_2 - \frac{\partial \mu_2^+}{\partial x}\right) = 0 \quad (3.74)$$

This equation has an important consequence. Instead of using the average mass velocity ω in the definition of the diffusion vectors (cf., 3.68), it is permissible to use any other reference velocity $\boldsymbol{\omega}_a$. The entropy production (3.73) remains invariant under any such change. For example, we can use as the reference velocity the macroscopic velocity of constituent 2. (3.73) then takes the simple form

$$\sigma = \frac{1}{T}\left(\mathfrak{F}_1 - \frac{\partial \mu_1^+}{\partial x}\right) \rho_1 \,(\omega_1 - \omega_2) > 0 \qquad (3.75)$$

Some applications of this formula will be found in Chapter V.

11. Internal Degrees of Freedom*

The thermodynamic formulae which have been developed in this chapter can be extended to irreversible processes related to internal degrees of freedom of the molecules such as deformation by flow, orientation by external alternating electrical fields, etc. Such phenomena are in the forefront of actual research problems concerning macromolecules and are presumably of great interest also for biological applications. We shall now indicate the extension of the thermodynamic formalism which is needed for our purpose. Our starting point will again be Gibbs' formula (3.17). We shall consider a one-component system in which the molecules may be in different internal states; γ now characterizes such a state (γ may be the angle which dipolar molecules form with an external field, or the length of a deformable molecule). Instead of taking discontinuous values, γ will generally have a continuous range of values so that (3.17) will be written in the continuous form

$$\frac{dS}{dt} = \frac{1}{T}\frac{dE}{dt} + \frac{p}{T}\frac{dV}{dt} - \frac{1}{T}\int_\gamma \mu(\gamma)\,\frac{\partial n(\gamma)}{\partial t}\,d\gamma \qquad (3.76)$$

* Section 11 is not used later in this book.

Here, $n(\gamma)$ is the density of molecules in the state γ so that $n(\gamma)\,d\gamma$ is the number of molecules for which the internal parameter lies between γ and $\gamma + d\gamma$.

We may transform (3.76) by using for $(\partial n(\gamma)/\partial t)$ a continuity equation analogous to (3.63). Suppose first that γ takes only discontinuous values and that the number of molecules in state γ may be altered only by transformations from or into the neighboring states $\gamma - 1$ or $\gamma + 1$. We should then have

$$\frac{dn_\gamma}{dt} + (\mathrm{v}_\gamma - \mathrm{v}_{\gamma-1}) = 0 \tag{3.77}$$

where v_γ is the rate of the reaction $\gamma \rightarrow (\gamma + 1)$ and at the same time $\mathrm{v}_{\gamma-1}$ is the rate of $\gamma - 1 \rightarrow \gamma$. If γ is a continuous parameter, (3.77) may be expressed as

$$\frac{\partial n(\gamma)}{\partial t} + \frac{\partial \mathrm{v}(\gamma)}{\partial \gamma} = 0 \tag{3.78}$$

where $\mathrm{v}(\gamma)$ is the reaction rate giving the number of molecules which are transformed from γ to $\gamma + d\gamma$ per unit time. This equation is analogous to (3.63) and is a continuity equation in the "internal coordinate space" γ. The reaction rate gives the flow of molecules along the coordinate γ. In vector notation (cf., (3.63), (3.64)), (3.78) may be written as

$$\frac{\partial n(\gamma)}{\partial t} = -\mathrm{div}\,\mathbf{v}\,(\gamma) \tag{3.78'}$$

Using (3.78), equation (3.76) may be transformed by a partial integration into

$$\frac{dS}{dt} = \frac{1}{T}\frac{dE}{dt} + \frac{p}{T}\frac{dV}{dt} - \frac{1}{T}\int_\gamma \frac{\partial \mu(\gamma)}{\partial \gamma}\,\mathrm{v}(\gamma)d\gamma \tag{3.79}$$

The last term is the entropy production due to the irreversible processes corresponding to changes of the internal parameter γ,

$$\frac{d_iS}{dt} = -\frac{1}{T}\int_\gamma \frac{\partial\mu(\gamma)}{\partial\gamma}\,\mathrm{v}(\gamma)d\gamma > 0 \tag{3.80}$$

At this point we can make a further refinement in the formulation of the second principle by postulating that not only the resultant entropy production due to the internal irreversible processes is positive but also that in each part of the internal coordinate space, the irreversible processes proceed in a direction such that a positive entropy production results. This formulation requires not only that the integral (3.80) is positive but also that the argument of the integral,

$$\sigma^* = -\frac{1}{T}\frac{\partial\mu(\gamma)}{\partial\gamma}\mathrm{v}(\gamma) > 0 \tag{3.81}$$

is positive; σ^* is the entropy production per unit volume of the internal configurational space, just as σ is the entropy production per unit volume of the ordinary geometrical space. The entropy production σ^* has the usual form. It is the product of the affinity $-\frac{1}{T}\frac{\partial\mu(\gamma)}{\partial\gamma}$ and the rate v (γ) of the irreversible process.

If there exists a potential energy which varies with γ (the internal coordinate γ may be the angle θ of a dipole with respect to an electrical field e, the potential energy of the dipole is then $E_{\text{pot}} = -me\cos\theta$ where m is the dipole moment) there then appears the corresponding "force" $-\frac{\partial E_{\text{pot}}}{\partial\gamma}$ in the entropy production, exactly as the forces $\mathfrak{F}_\gamma$ appear in (3.72). We thus have

$$\sigma^* = -\frac{1}{T}\left(\frac{\partial\mu(\gamma)}{\partial\gamma} + \frac{\partial E_{\text{pot}}}{\partial\gamma}\right)\mathrm{v}(\gamma) > 0 \tag{3.82}$$

By the use of a linear relation between the rate v (γ) and the affinity $-\frac{1}{T}\left(\frac{\partial\mu(\gamma)}{\partial\gamma}+\frac{\partial E_{\text{pot}}}{\partial\gamma}\right)$ as explained in Chapters IV and V, it is easy to obtain a thermodynamic formulation of Debye's theory of orientation of dipoles in an electrical alternative field.

Our formulation (3.81) expresses that the entropy production per unit volume of the internal configuration space is essentially positive. This is again an example of the local formulation of the second principle of thermodynamics to which we have already referred in § 2 of this chapter.

The possibility of such a local formulation depends clearly on the mechanism of the irreversible processes we are studying. If collisions between dipoles alter the angle θ by finite amounts we cannot expect (3.81) to hold, because in this case the irreversible increase of the entropy density σ^* (θ) depends on the number of dipoles for different values of the angle θ. But if collisions alter the angle by a very small amount, the total effect being due to the cumulative action of a large number of collisions such a local formulation is exact. This example is instructive as it shows the limitation to a local formulation of the second principle (for more details and the relation to the usual treatment of irreversible processes, e.g., visco-elastic behaviour of polymers, cf. [19]). We have now completed the evaluation of the entropy production for some important and typical cases. The rest of this book is devoted to a further analysis of the entropy production and to applications.

CHAPTER IV

General Statements Concerning Entropy Production and Rates of Irreversible Processes

1. Transformation Properties of Rates and Affinities—Equivalent Systems

In the preceding chapter we have shown that entropy production can be written as a sum of the products of generalized forces or affinities and the corresponding rates (or generalized "fluxes") of the irreversible processes

$$\frac{d_iS}{dt} = \sum_k J_k X_k > 0 \tag{4.1}$$

We have here adopted a standard notation in which we denote the generalized forces by X_k and the rates by J_k, while the symbol A is reserved for the chemical affinity as defined by (3.22). With this new notation, for instance, the entropy production due to a chemical reaction may be written as*

$$\frac{d_iS}{dt} = J_{\text{ch}} X_{\text{ch}} \qquad \text{with} \qquad J_{\text{ch}} = \text{v}, \qquad X_{\text{ch}} = \frac{A}{T} \tag{4.2}$$

The next few sections will be devoted to a study of the quantitative relations between the affinities and the rates

* Though it would conform more to these general notations to call A/T the chemical affinity, we shall continue, for historical reasons, to call A the chemical affinity.

of irreversible processes. It is imperative, however, that we first investigate to what extent these quantities are defined.

Let us consider as a particular example a system in which two "isomerisations"

$$A \rightarrow B \quad (1), \qquad B \rightarrow C \quad (2) \tag{4.3}$$

take place. The corresponding affinities are (cf., 3.22)

$$A_1 = \mu_A - \mu_B, \qquad A_2 = \mu_B - \mu_C \tag{4.4}$$

and the change per unit time of the mole numbers, as a result of reactions (1) and (2), is given by relation (1.6) in which both members are divided by dt

$$\frac{dn_A}{dt} = -v_1; \qquad \frac{dn_B}{dt} = v_1 - v_2; \qquad \frac{dn_C}{dt} = v_2 \tag{4.5}$$

The corresponding entropy production is

$$T\frac{d_iS}{dt} = A_1v_1 + A_2v_2 > 0 \tag{4.6}$$

It is quite clear that from the macroscopic point of view the chemical changes could be equally well described by the two reactions

$$A \rightarrow C \quad (1'), \qquad B \rightarrow C \quad (2') \tag{4.7}$$

which are linear combinations of the reactions (4.3). The new affinities, corresponding to (4.7) are related to the old ones by

$$\left.\begin{aligned} A_1' &= \mu_A - \mu_C = A_1 + A_2 \\ A_2' &= \mu_B - \mu_C = A_2 \end{aligned}\right\} \tag{4.8}$$

This transformation law shows that chemical affinities transform like the corresponding stoichiometric equations.

To obtain the corresponding transformation law for the reaction rates, we apply to (4.7) the formula for changes of mole numbers (1.6)

$$\frac{dn_A}{dt} = -v_1'; \qquad \frac{dn_B}{dt} = -v_2'; \qquad \frac{dn_C}{dt} = v_1' + v_2' \qquad (4.9)$$

Then comparing (4.5) and (4.9) we find that

$$\left.\begin{aligned} v_1 &= v_1' \\ v_2 &= v_1' + v_2' \end{aligned}\right\} \qquad (4.10)$$

This transformation law for the reaction rates is complementary to that of the affinities in such a way as to maintain the entropy production invariant

$$T\frac{d_iS}{dt} = A_1v_1 + A_2v_2 = A_1'v_1' + A_2'v_2' \qquad (4.11)$$

The equation can be readily checked by substituting the new affinities and reaction rates from (4.8) and (4.10).

From our thermodynamic point of view the description by (4.3) is equivalent to (4.7) and we may call such systems "*equivalent systems*" [20, 21, 22].

The preceding considerations can be easily generalized. Supposing that we had written the entropy production in formula (4.1) by using a given set of affinities X_k and corresponding rates J_k, we may then introduce a new set of affinities X_k' which are linear combinations of the old ones and choose a new set of rates J_k' in such a way that the entropy production is invariant.*

$$\sum_k J_kX_k = \sum_k J_k'X_k' \qquad (4.12)$$

The description in terms of (J_k, X_k) is macroscopically equivalent to that in terms of (J_k', X_k'). An alternative

* The only condition of the invariance of entropy production may not be sufficient to assure the equivalent character of the two descriptions (J_k, X_k) and (J_k', X_k'). In our example we used also the invariance of the rate of change of the number of moles n_A, n_B, n_C (eqs. 4.5 and 4.9). This is necessary to avoid certain paradoxes to which Verschaffelt [60] has called attention (cf., also [61]).

procedure would be to introduce first a new set of rates J'_k, which are linear combinations of the old ones and then to choose the new X'_k in order to satisfy (4.12).

As an example, we shall take the entropy production (3.53) but for convenience we shall omit the terms which correspond to chemical reactions. Using the notation (4.1) we can then write

$$\frac{d_iS}{dt} = JX + \sum_\gamma J_\gamma X_\gamma \tag{4.13}$$

with

$$J = -\frac{d_i^{\mathrm{I}}\Phi}{dt} = \frac{d_i^{\mathrm{II}}\Phi}{dt}; \qquad J_\gamma = -\frac{d_e n_\gamma^{\mathrm{I}}}{dt} = \frac{d_e n_\gamma^{\mathrm{II}}}{dt} \tag{4.14}$$

$$X = \frac{1}{T^{\mathrm{II}}} - \frac{1}{T^{\mathrm{I}}} = \Delta\left(\frac{1}{T}\right);$$
$$X_\gamma = -\left(\frac{\mu_\gamma^{\mathrm{II}}}{T^{\mathrm{II}}} - \frac{\mu_\gamma^{\mathrm{I}}}{T^{\mathrm{I}}}\right) = -\Delta\left(\frac{\mu_\gamma}{T}\right) \tag{4.15}$$

We shall now introduce new fluxes

$$\left.\begin{aligned} J' &= J - \sum_\gamma h_\gamma J_\gamma \\ J'_\gamma &= J_\gamma \end{aligned}\right\} \tag{4.16}$$

Utilizing the invariance relation

$$JX + \sum_\gamma J_\gamma X_\gamma = J'X' + \sum_\gamma J'_\gamma X'_\gamma \tag{4.17}$$

it is then readily found that we have to take for the new affinities

$$\left.\begin{aligned} X' &= X = \Delta\left(\frac{1}{T}\right) \\ X'_\gamma &= X_\gamma + h_\gamma X = -\Delta\left(\frac{\mu_\gamma}{T}\right) + h_\gamma \Delta\left(\frac{1}{T}\right) \end{aligned}\right\} \tag{4.18}$$

Bearing in mind that

$$\Delta\left(\frac{\mu_\gamma}{T}\right) = \frac{\partial(\mu_\gamma/T)}{\partial T}\,\Delta T + \frac{(\Delta\mu_\gamma)_T}{T} \tag{4.19}$$

and with the third of relations (3.21), X'_γ becomes

$$X'_\gamma = -\,\frac{(\Delta\mu_\gamma)_T}{T} \tag{4.20}$$

The affinities X' and X'_γ may be used instead of the original ones for the description of the irreversible transport of matter and energy between the two phases.

The study of the transformation laws for affinities and rates is important because often different authors have studied the same irreversible process but have used different equivalent systems so that the identity of their results is not always immediately obvious (for a very careful survey of this question, see de Groot [18]). It also often happens that one particular choice is more convenient than others.* For example, the set X', X'_γ has an advantage over the set X, X_γ in that it is well defined numerically while X_γ, still containing h_γ (see 4.19, and 3.21), includes an arbitrary additive constant (cf., 2.16).

2. Rates and Affinities

We now return to the general expression for the entropy production (4.1). At thermodynamic equilibrium, we have simultaneously for *all* irreversible processes

$$J_k = 0 \qquad \text{and} \qquad X_k = 0 \tag{4.21}$$

It is quite natural to assume, at least close to equilibrium, that we have linear relations between the rates and the

* A very significant example is provided by the thermodynamic study of thermomagnetic and galvanomagnetic effects. By using a particularly well-adapted system of affinities and rates, it is possible to obtain readily the thermodynamic relations between these effects, a result which was difficult to obtain by other methods [23].

affinities. Such a scheme automatically includes empirical laws as Fourier's law for heat flow or Fick's law for diffusion. In the next chapter we shall study many examples of such linear laws and we shall also discuss their domain of validity. Linear laws of this kind are called the *phenomenological relations.* It is clear that the existence of such relations is an extra-thermodynamic hypothesis and it is quite conceivable that in some particular cases the relationship between flow and affinity may not be linear.* However, once that linear relations have been introduced, our thermodynamic methods will yield important information concerning the coefficients which appear in these relations without invoking any particular kinetic model.

To illustrate this point we now consider the case of two simultaneous irreversible processes, for which two phenomenological relations may be written down

$$\left.\begin{aligned} J_1 &= L_{11}X_1 + L_{12}X_2 \\ J_2 &= L_{21}X_1 + L_{22}X_2 \end{aligned}\right\} \tag{4.22}$$

The coefficients L_{ik} are called the *phenomenological coefficients.* The coefficients L_{ii} may stand for the heat conductivity, the electrical conductivity, the chemical drag coefficient, while the coefficients L_{ik} (with $i \neq k$) describe the *interference* of the two irreversible processes i and k. If the two irreversible processes represent thermal conductivity and diffusion, the coefficient L_{ik} (in the next section we will prove that $L_{ik} = L_{ki}$) is connected with thermodiffusion, that is, with the appearance of a concentration gradient in an initially homogeneous mix-

* For example, the friction which acts on a light Brownian particle in a rarefied gas may depend nonlinearly on the velocity of the particle (cf., [24]) Then for mechanical equilibrium (zero acceleration) there is also no linear relation between the velocity of the particle and an external force acting on it. But for small velocities this relation reduces to a linear one.

ture under the influence of a temperature gradient. Throughout this chapter, we shall investigate the general properties of these "*interference coefficients.*" We shall first examine certain limitations imposed on these coefficients by the second principle of thermodynamics.

Replacing the fluxes by their value (4.22) in the entropy production (4.1), we obtained the quadratic form

$$\frac{d_iS}{dt} = L_{11}X_1^2 + (L_{12} + L_{21})X_1X_2 + L_{22}X_2^2 > 0 \qquad (4.23)$$

This quadratic form has to be positive for all positive or negative values of the variables X_1, X_2 except when $X_1 = X_2 = 0$, in which case the entropy production vanishes. It is shown in elementary textbooks on algebra that the coefficients L_{ik} must satisfy the following inequalities

$$L_{11} > 0, \qquad L_{22} > 0 \qquad (4.24)$$

$$(L_{12} + L_{21})^2 < 4L_{11}L_{22} \qquad (4.25)$$

Hence the "proper" phenomenological coefficients (L_{11}, L_{22}) are positive. On the other hand, the "mutual" coefficients (L_{12}, L_{21}) may be positive or negative, their magnitude being limited only by (4.25). This is in agreement with the empirical observation that coefficients, like thermal conductivity, or electrical conductivity, are always positive while, for example, the thermodiffusion coefficient has no definite sign.

We shall now formulate an important theorem due to Onsager (1931) [62] which states that

$$L_{ik} = L_{ki} \qquad (i, k = 1 \ldots n) \qquad (4.26)$$

These Onsager reciprocity relations express that when the flux, corresponding to the irreversible processes i, is influenced by the affinity X_k of the irreversible process k, then the flux k is also influenced by the affinity X_i through the same interference coefficient L_{ik}.

Some preliminary considerations are necessary before the derivation of (4.26) can be given. First, we shall briefly study the fluctuation theory of an "aged" system, i.e., a system which has been left isolated for a length of time sufficient to ensure thermodynamic equilibrium (§ 3). We shall then be concerned with *microscopic reversibility*, i.e., the symmetry of all mechanical equations of motion of individual particles with respect to time (§ 4). The reader interested in the applications only can accept Onsager reciprocity relations as a supplementary principle and continue with § 5.

3. Fluctuation Theory

Consider a system characterized by r degrees of advancement $\xi_1 \ldots \xi_r$. The deviations of the ξ_ρ from their equilibrium values ξ_ρ^e will be denoted by α_ρ. Instead of degrees of advancement, we might also adopt local temperature, pressure, etc., as fluctuating parameters. For convenience however we shall present the argument by using the degrees of advancement as parameters. The generalization is trivial.

The entropy change due to the fluctuation α is

$$\Delta_i S = \int_{\xi^e}^{\xi} d_i S = \int_{\xi^e}^{\xi} \frac{A}{T} d\xi \tag{4.27}$$

A may be expanded in a Taylor series and since $A(\xi^e) = 0$, considering only the linear term in $\xi - \xi^e$ we obtain

$$A = \left(\frac{\partial A}{\partial \xi}\right)_e (\xi - \xi^e)$$

(4.27) therefore becomes

$$\Delta_i S = \frac{1}{2}\left(\frac{\partial A}{\partial \xi}\right)_e \alpha^2/T \tag{4.27'}$$

or
$$\Delta_i S = \frac{1}{2} A\alpha/T$$

The coefficient $^1/_2$ is due to the integration in (4.27). $\Delta_i S$ is always *negative.* Indeed, if $\Delta_i S$ were positive, the transformation $\xi_\rho^e \rightarrow \xi_\rho$ would be a spontaneous irreversible change and thus be incompatible with our assumption that the initial state is an equilibrium state. For simultaneous fluctuations ($\rho = 1 \ldots r$), we find similarly*

$$\Delta_i S = \frac{1}{2T} \sum_{\rho\rho'} \left(\frac{\partial A_\rho}{\partial \xi_{\rho'}}\right)_e \alpha_{\rho'}\, \alpha_\rho < 0 \tag{4.28}$$

Using the abreviation

$$g_{\rho\rho'} = -\frac{1}{T} \left(\frac{\partial A_\rho}{\partial \xi_{\rho'}}\right)_e \tag{4.29}$$

(4.28) may be written as

$$\Delta_i S = -\frac{1}{2} \sum_{\rho\rho'} g_{\rho\rho'} \alpha_\rho \alpha_{\rho'} < 0 \tag{4.30}$$

We note also that

$$\frac{A_\rho}{T} = \frac{1}{T} \sum_{\rho'} \left(\frac{\partial A_\rho}{\partial \xi_{\rho'}}\right)_e \alpha_{\rho'} = \frac{\partial \Delta_i S}{\partial \alpha_\rho} \tag{4.31}$$

Again, using the notation (4.2)

$$X_\rho = -\sum_{\rho'} g_{\rho\rho'} \alpha_{\rho'} = \frac{\partial \Delta_i S}{\partial \alpha_\rho} \tag{4.31'}$$

Solving the α_ρ from these equations, we get

$$\alpha_\rho = -\sum_{\rho'} g_{\rho\rho'}^{-1} X_{\rho'} \tag{4.32}$$

where $g_{\rho\rho'}^{-1}$ is the so-called *"reciprocal" matrix* of $g_{\rho\rho'}$. Equation (4.30) is of a fairly general nature. Only the explicit values of the coefficients $g_{\rho\rho'}$ depend on the nature

* For further details cf., [9a], Chapter XV.

of the fluctuating parameters. In the system under consideration, the probability P of fluctuations $\Delta\xi_\rho$ is proportional to the exponential of the corresponding entropy deviation $\Delta_i S$ (Einstein's fluctuation theory*) divided by Boltzmann's constant k.

It follows that the probability of finding a state in which the values of the α_ρ lie between α_ρ and $d\alpha_\rho$ is given by

$$P d\alpha_1 \ldots d\alpha_r = \frac{\exp \Delta_i S/k \cdot d\alpha_1 \ldots d\alpha_r}{\int \ldots \int \exp \Delta_i S/k \cdot d\alpha_1 \ldots d\alpha_r} \tag{4.33}$$

The denominator on the right hand ensures normalization to unity

$$\int \ldots \int P d\alpha_1 \ldots d\alpha_r = 1 \tag{4.34}$$

We now calculate the following average

$$\overline{X_\rho \alpha_{\rho'}} = \int \ldots \int X_\rho \alpha_{\rho'} P d\alpha_1 \ldots d\alpha_r \tag{4.35}$$

Taking into account (4.31′) and (4.33) we can write

$$\begin{aligned} \overline{X_\rho \alpha_{\rho'}} &= k \int \ldots \int \alpha_{\rho'} \frac{\partial \log P}{\partial \alpha_\rho} P d\alpha_1 \ldots d\alpha_r \\ &= k \int \ldots \int d\alpha_1 \ldots d\alpha_{\rho-1} d\alpha_{\rho+1} \ldots d\alpha_r \int \alpha_{\rho'} \frac{\partial P}{\partial \alpha_\rho} d\alpha_\rho \end{aligned} \tag{4.36}$$

Partial integration over α_ρ gives

$$\int_{-\infty}^{+\infty} \alpha_{\rho'} \frac{\partial P}{\partial \alpha_\rho} d\alpha_\rho = [\alpha_{\rho'} P]_{-\infty}^{+\infty} - \int_{-\infty}^{+\infty} P \frac{\partial \alpha_{\rho'}}{\partial \alpha_\rho} d\alpha_\rho \tag{4.37}$$

P is zero for $\alpha_\rho = \pm \infty$. Moreover, since $\alpha_{\rho'}$ and α_ρ are

---

* For a discussion of Einstein's fluctuation theory, cf., Tolman [25], Fowler [26] and especially Greene [27]. Our formulation of this theorem introduces the entropy production due to fluctuations and is slightly more general than the usual formulation which applies only to some particular transformations such as adiabatic or isothermal changes (cf., also [9a], Chapter XV).

independent variables, we have in the second integral

$$\frac{\partial \alpha_{\rho'}}{\partial \alpha_\rho} = \delta_{\rho'\rho} \qquad \text{with } \delta_{\rho'\rho} \begin{cases} = 1 \text{ for } \rho' = \rho \\ = 0 \text{ for } \rho' \neq \rho \end{cases} \tag{4.38}$$

so that

$$\overline{X_\rho \alpha_{\rho'}} = -k \int \ldots \int d\alpha_1 \ldots d\alpha_{\rho-1} d\alpha_{\rho+1} \ldots d\alpha_r \int P \delta_{\rho'\rho} d\alpha_\rho \tag{4.39}$$

With the normalization condition (4.34), this becomes

$$\overline{X_\rho \alpha_{\rho'}} = -k\delta_{\rho'\rho} \tag{4.40}$$

We shall require this result later on. Other averages can be calculated for instance from (4.40). By using (4.31′)

$$\overline{X_\rho X_{\rho'}} = -\sum_{\rho''} g_{\rho\rho''} \overline{\alpha_{\rho''} \cdot X_{\rho'}} = k g_{\rho\rho'} \tag{4.41}$$

and also (see 4.32)

$$\overline{\alpha_\rho \alpha_{\rho'}} = -\sum_{\rho''} g_{\rho\rho''}^{-1} \overline{X_{\rho''} \alpha_{\rho'}} = k g_{\rho\rho'}^{-1} \tag{4.42}$$

These relations show that the coefficients $g_{\rho\rho'}$ or $g_{\rho\rho'}^{-1}$ have an interesting physical meaning in that they are related to the fluctuations in a system close to thermodynamical equilibrium. For a single irreversible process, (4.40)–(4.42) become

$$\overline{X\alpha} = -k, \qquad \overline{X^2} = kg, \qquad \overline{\alpha^2} = \frac{k}{g} \tag{4.43}$$

It is also interesting to note that fluctuation phenomena are accompanied by an average decrease of entropy since this quantity, according to (4.28)–(4.31) and (4.40), is given by

$$\overline{\Delta_i S} = \frac{1}{2} \sum_\rho \overline{X_\rho \alpha_\rho} = -\frac{1}{2} rk \tag{4.44}$$

This result, which bears a close resemblance to the equipartition theorem of classical statistical mechanics expresses that each irreversible process contributes the same term $-k/2$ to the average decrease of entropy due to fluctuations.

Explicit formulae for fluctuation of chemical affinities and degrees of advancement may be found elsewhere [28].

4. Microscopic Reversibility and Onsager's Reciprocity Relations

The principal property of microscopic reversibility consists in the invariance of all mechanical equations of motion of individual particles with respect to the transformation $t \to -t$.*

We now consider the value of the fluctuation α_i at a time instant t and of fluctuation α_j after a time interval τ and we form the product of both quantities. The average value of this product during a sufficiently long lapse of time is given by

$$\overline{\alpha_i(t)\alpha_j(t+\tau)} = \lim_{T\to\infty} \frac{1}{T} \int_0^T \alpha_i(t)\alpha_j(t+\tau)dt \quad (4.45)$$

Following the general principles of statistical mechanics, it can be shown that the time average (4.45) is equivalent to the average taken with the help of probability function P (4.33) (this is the so-called "ergodic theorem" [30]).

We next consider the average value of the product $\alpha_j(t)\alpha_i(t+\tau)$ in which we consider the fluctuations $\alpha_j(t)$ and $\alpha_i(t+\tau)$, the latter occurring after the time interval τ. The mean value $\overline{\alpha_j(t)\alpha_i(t+\tau)}$ differs from (4.45) only by the temporal order of the two fluctuations, or more briefly by the substitution $t \to -t$. So we shall express the microscopic reversibility by the formula

* The reconciliation of macroscopic irreversibility with microscopic reversibility is a very important problem of statistical mechanics. For an excellent discussion of this point in the case of Brownian motion, see Chandrasekhar [29]. For a general discussion see Khinchin [30].

$$\overline{\alpha_i(t)\alpha_j(t+\tau)} = \overline{\alpha_j(t)\alpha_i(t+\tau)} \tag{4.46}$$

Subtracting the same quantity $\overline{\alpha_i(t)\alpha_j(t)}$ from both members of equation (4.46) and dividing by τ, we have

$$\overline{\alpha_i(t)\,\frac{[\alpha_j(t+\tau) - \alpha_j(t)]}{\tau}} = \overline{\alpha_j(t)\,\frac{[\alpha_i(t+\tau) - \alpha_i(t)]}{\tau}} \tag{4.47}$$

When τ tends to zero, we obtain

$$\overline{\alpha_i(t)\dot{\alpha}_j(t)} = \overline{\alpha_j(t)\dot{\alpha}_i(t)} \tag{4.48}$$

Strictly speaking, the time derivative, denoted by the dot in (4.48), must be considered as a quotient of differences because the value of τ must always be superior to a characteristic molecular time τ_0 which is of the same order as the time interval between two collisions of molecules.

We shall assume that decay of a fluctuation $\dot{\alpha}_i$ follows the ordinary macroscopic linear laws (4.22) and write

$$J_i = \dot{\alpha}_i = \sum_k L_{ik} X_k \tag{4.49}$$

Introducing (4.49) into (4.48) we get

$$\sum_k L_{jk} \overline{\alpha_i X_k} = \sum_k L_{jk} \overline{\alpha_j X_k} \tag{4.50}$$

and taking account of (4.40), these relations reduce to

$$L_{ji} = L_{ij} \tag{4.51}$$

i.e., the Onsager relations which we sought. Although they have been proved here for small spontaneous fluctuations around thermodynamic equilibrium only, we shall accept the validity of Onsager's relations even for systems with systematic deviations from equilibrium (for example, a system in which we maintain a temperature gradient), as long as the relations between fluxes and affinities remain linear.

The extension of Onsager's reciprocity relation to the case of an external magnetic field will not be considered here (cf. [62]). We shall ignore also the formal difficulties which arise when the Onsager principle is extended to continuous systems and which have been elucidated by Casimir [31]. This topic is excellently reviewed in de Groot's monograph [18].

5. Symmetry Requirements on Coupling of Irreversible Processes

In section 2 we introduced the phenomenological coefficients L_{ik} (with $i \neq k$) which describe the interference of the two irreversible processes i and k. Onsager's reciprocity relation (4.51) shows that the coefficients L_{ik} and L_{ki} which express this interference are equal: $L_{ki} = L_{ik}$. We shall now specify which irreversible processes are capable of mutual interference. For convenience, we shall consider a continuous system without diffusion but with a heat flow along the geometrical coordinate x and subject at the same time to a chemical reaction. According to (3.72) the entropy production is

$$\sigma = -\frac{W_x}{T^2}\frac{\partial T}{\partial x} + \frac{A \mathrm{v}_v}{T} > 0 \tag{4.52}$$

The phenomenological relations are

$$\left.\begin{aligned} W_x &= -\frac{L_{\mathrm{th}}}{T^2}\frac{\partial T}{\partial x} + L_{12}\frac{A}{T} \\ \mathrm{v}_v &= -\frac{L_{21}}{T^2}\frac{\partial T}{\partial x} + L_{\mathrm{ch}}\frac{A}{T} \end{aligned}\right\} \tag{4.53}$$

A first reduction of the number of phenomenological coefficients is obtained by the Onsager reciprocity relations, which give $L_{12} = L_{21}$. In this case, however, we can specify some additional condition and show that

$$L_{12} = L_{21} = 0 \tag{4.54}$$

Suppose that $\partial T/\partial x = 0$; (4.53) then gives

$$W_x = L_{12} \frac{A}{T} \tag{4.55}$$

so that the scalar "cause" A/T would produce the vectorial "effect" W_x. This would be contrary to the general requirements of symmetry principles (Curie's symmetry principles: P. Curie [32]) according to which macroscopic causes always have fewer elements of symmetry than the effects they produce. Chemical affinity therefore cannot produce a directed heat flow and the interference coefficient must necessarily be zero.

In a case like this not only is the total entropy production due to all irreversible processes positive but there are some irreversible processes or groups of irreversible processes which give separate positive contributions to the total entropy production. In (4.52) we have separately

$$-\frac{W_x}{T^2}\frac{\partial T}{\partial x} > 0 \qquad \text{and} \qquad \frac{A\mathrm{v}_v}{T} > 0 \tag{4.56}$$

In the entropy production (3.53) we can even distinguish three contributions, each positive. The first is due to directed transport phenomena from phase^{I} to phase^{II},

$$\left(\frac{1}{T^{\mathrm{I}}} - \frac{1}{T^{\mathrm{II}}}\right)\frac{d_i^{\mathrm{I}}\Phi}{dt} - \sum_\gamma \left(\frac{\mu_\gamma^{\mathrm{I}}}{T^{\mathrm{I}}} - \frac{\mu_\gamma^{\mathrm{II}}}{T^{\mathrm{II}}}\right)\frac{d_e n_\gamma^{\mathrm{I}}}{dt} > 0 \tag{4.57}$$

The second and third contributions are due to chemical reactions in different phases

$$\frac{A^{\mathrm{I}}\mathrm{v}^{\mathrm{I}}}{T^{\mathrm{I}}} > 0, \qquad \frac{A^{\mathrm{II}}\mathrm{v}^{\mathrm{II}}}{T^{\mathrm{II}}} > 0 \tag{4.58}$$

Such a decomposition is very useful as it enables us to recognize which irreversible processes may be directly coupled through interference coefficients.

CHAPTER V

The Phenomenological Laws—Interference of Irreversible Processes

1. Domain of Validity of Phenomenological Laws—Chemical Reactions Near Equilibrium

In the preceding chapter we introduced phenomenological linear relations between fluxes or rates of irreversible processes and affinities. In order to obtain a better understanding of the domain of validity of such linear laws, we shall consider two examples.

We shall first examine a simple *transport process*, the heat flow in a continuous system. The entropy production per unit time and per unit volume is given by (3.72). Ignoring diffusion processes and chemical reactions, we have simply (cf., 4.52)

$$\sigma = -\frac{W_x}{T^2}\frac{\partial T}{\partial x} > 0 \tag{5.1}$$

with the corresponding phenomenological relation

$$W_x = -\frac{L}{T^2}\frac{\partial T}{\partial x} \tag{5.2}$$

As this is simply Fourier's law, with the heat conductivity

$$\lambda = -\frac{L}{T^2} \tag{5.3}$$

the domain of validity of the phenomenological law (5.2) is just the same as the validity of Fourier's law and can be discussed in a thorough way in the case of gases, for which a detailed statistical theory is available (cf. [12, 34]). It can be shown that (5.2) is valid whenever the relative variation of temperature is small within a length equal to the mean free path φ

$$\frac{\varphi}{T}\frac{\partial T}{\partial x} \ll 1 \tag{5.4}$$

This condition is satisfied in most of the usual cases [12] and in general the phenomenological laws may be considered to give good approximations for transport processes.

Next, we shall consider the case of chemical reactions. For a single chemical reaction the phenomenological relation is

$$\mathrm{v} = L\frac{A}{T} \tag{5.5}$$

with the corresponding entropy production

$$\frac{d_iS}{dt} = L\left(\frac{A}{T}\right)^2 \tag{5.6}$$

In order to compare the phenomenological law (5.5) with the usual kinetic expressions for reaction rate, we shall consider the simple case of the synthesis of hydriodic acid in the gaseous phase. (Other examples of chemical reactions will be studied in Chapter VI.) The chemical reaction is

$$\mathrm{H_2 + I_2 = 2HI} \tag{5.7}$$

And the corresponding affinity (cf., 3.27)

$$A = \mu_{\mathrm{H_2}} + \mu_{\mathrm{I_2}} - 2\mu_{\mathrm{HI}} \tag{5.8}$$

According to (3.23) and (3.24), the chemical potentials for a mixture of perfect gases may be written in the form

$$\mu_\gamma = \eta_\gamma(T) + RT \log C_\gamma \tag{5.9}$$

Introducing the equilibrium constant of the reaction K (cf. 3.40)

$$RT \log K(T) = -\sum_\gamma \nu_\gamma \eta_\gamma(T) \tag{5.10}$$

the affinity becomes (cf., 3.41)

$$\begin{aligned} A &= -\sum_\gamma \nu_\gamma \eta_\gamma(T) - RT \sum_\gamma \nu_\gamma \log C_\gamma \\ &= RT \log \frac{K(T)}{C_1^{\nu_1} \ldots C_c^{\nu_c}} \end{aligned} \tag{5.11}$$

For the synthesis of HI, it follows from (5.11) that

$$A = RT \log \frac{K(T)}{C_{I_2}^{-1} C_{H_2}^{-1} C_{HI}^2} \tag{5.12}$$

The usual kinetic expression for the reaction rate of (5.7) is given by

$$\mathrm{v} = \overrightarrow{\mathrm{v}} - \overleftarrow{\mathrm{v}} = \overrightarrow{k} C_{I_2} C_{H_2} - \overleftarrow{k} C_{HI}^2 = \overrightarrow{k} C_{I_2} C_{H_2} \left(1 - \frac{\overleftarrow{k}}{\overrightarrow{k}} \frac{C_{HI}^2}{C_{I_2} C_{H_2}}\right) \tag{5.13}$$

It is well known that the ratio of the kinetic constants $\overrightarrow{k}/\overleftarrow{k}$ is equal to the equilibrium constant so that (5.13) can be written as (cf. 5.12)

$$\mathrm{v} = \overrightarrow{\mathrm{v}} \left(1 - \exp\left(-\frac{A}{RT}\right)\right) \tag{5.14}$$

This equation expresses fairly generally the relation between reaction rate and affinity. For reactions close to equilibrium

$$\left| \frac{A}{RT} \right| \ll 1 \tag{5.15}$$

and formula (5.14) reduces to

$$\text{v} = \frac{\overrightarrow{\text{v}}^e}{R} \frac{A}{T} \tag{5.16}$$

where $\overrightarrow{\text{v}}^e$ is the value of the partial rate $\overrightarrow{\text{v}}$ at equilibrium ($\overrightarrow{\text{v}}^e = \overleftarrow{\text{v}}^e$ for $A = 0$). It can now be seen that inequality (5.15) gives the condition for the validity of the linear law (5.5), in which the coefficient L has a very simple physical meaning

$$L = \frac{\overrightarrow{\text{v}}^e}{R} \tag{5.17}$$

its value depending only on the value of $\overrightarrow{\text{v}}$ at equilibrium.

Let us consider the other extreme case, corresponding to

$$\frac{A}{RT} \rightarrow \infty \tag{5.18}$$

In a more explicit form, this condition means that (cf., 5.12)

$$\frac{C_{I_2}C_{H_2}}{C_{HI}^2} \rightarrow \infty \qquad \text{or} \qquad C_{HI} \rightarrow 0 \tag{5.19}$$

which for a closed system corresponds to the initial stage of the reaction. The corresponding value of v is simply (cf. 5.14)

$$\text{v} \rightarrow \overrightarrow{\text{v}} \tag{5.20}$$

and thus becomes independent of the affinity. This situation corresponds to a sort of *saturation effect* with respect to the affinity and, in the region in which it appears, the entropy production becomes a *linear* function of the affinity.

In contrast to the simple behavior of transport processes, the linear relations between rates and affinities are not always sufficient and in many cases it is necessary to take into account non-linear relations like (5.14).

However, when the affinity of a given chemical reaction is large, so that (5.15) is not satisfied, the reaction may often be split into a certain number of elementary reactions having each affinity sufficiently small to justify the application of the linear phenomenological laws. As an example, we consider a reaction of the form

$$M \rightarrow F$$

which proceeds in a number of succesive steps

$$\begin{array}{ll} M \rightarrow N & (1) \\ N \rightarrow O & (2) \\ \cdot & \cdot \\ \cdot & \cdot \\ \cdot & \cdot \\ P \rightarrow F & (r) \end{array}$$

The entropy production due to these succesive reactions is given by

$$T\frac{d_iS}{dt} = A_1\mathrm{v}_1 + A_2\mathrm{v}_2 \ldots + A_r\mathrm{v}_r$$

If the intermediate components $N, O, \ldots P$ are unstable, a stationary state

$$\mathrm{v}_1 = \mathrm{v}_2 = \ldots = \mathrm{v}_r = \mathrm{v}$$

is established after a short lapse of time, so that the entropy after production becomes

$$T \frac{d_i S}{dt} = A\text{v}$$

Here
$$A = \sum_\rho A_\rho$$

is the macroscopic affinity corresponding to the resultant change. Provided that

$$\frac{|A_\rho|}{RT} \ll 1 \tag{5.21}$$

we are still in the domain of validity of the linear phenomenological laws between reaction rates and affinities, even if for the total affinity

$$\frac{|A|}{RT} \gg 1 \tag{5.22}$$

Some examples of systems with chemical reactions will be studied in Chapter VI. In connection with the preceding considerations, it is of some interest that biological systems have often been assumed to be characterized by processes which usually take place in many steps, each of which is nearly reversible, so that (5.21) is satisfied (cf. [35]).

The formal kinetic equations become very simple near equilibrium, even for systems of complicated reactions and this leads to some interesting applications [36, 37, 38, 39]. For a closed system, the phenomenological law (5.5) can also be written as (cf. 1.4)

$$\frac{d\xi}{dt} = \frac{L}{T} A = \frac{L}{T} \left(\frac{\partial A}{\partial \xi}\right)_e (\xi - \xi_e) \tag{5.23}$$

Introducing the relaxation time τ

$$\tau = - \frac{T}{L \left(\frac{\partial A}{\partial \xi}\right)_e} \tag{5.24}$$

and integrating (5.23), we obtain an exponential time variation

$$\xi - \xi_e = (\xi - \xi_e)_0 \exp - \frac{t}{\tau} \tag{5.25}$$

Note that the relaxation time τ is positive ($\partial A/\partial\xi < 0$, cf. Chapter IV § 3).

In the general case of two simultaneous reactions each degree of advancement can be represented similarly as a superposition of r exponential functions of time having the form

$$\xi_\rho - \xi_{\rho,e} = \sum_{\rho'} a_{\rho\rho'} \exp -t/\tau_{\rho'} \tag{5.26}$$

A general demonstration will be found in a paper by Meixner [39]. The form (5.26) makes it possible to obtain some general information without detailed knowledge of the kinetic process. It can be shown, for example, that whatever the initial conditions, ξ_ρ can only cross its equilibrium value $\xi_{\rho,e}$, $(r - 1)$ times at the utmost and therefore a behavior, periodic in time, is impossible with a finite number of reactions.

2. Electrokinetic Effects—Saxen's Relation

By means of Onsager's reciprocity relation (4.26), we shall now study some examples of interference between irreversible processes. As a first example, we shall treat the connection between the various electrokinetic effects which has been examined by Mazur and Overbeek [40]. Consider a system consisting of two vessels I and II, which communicate by means of a porous wall or a capillary. The temperature and the concentrations are supposed to be uniform throughout the entire system and both phases differ only with respect to pressure and electrical potentials. The entropy production, due to the transfer of the constituents from vessel I to vessel II, is given by (cf. 3.61)

$$d_iS = \frac{1}{T}\sum_\gamma \tilde{A}_\gamma d\xi_\gamma = -\frac{1}{T}\sum_\gamma \tilde{A}_\gamma dn_\gamma^{\mathrm{I}} \qquad (5.27)$$

where $\tilde{A}_\gamma$ is the electrochemical affinity given by (3.59)

$$\tilde{A}_\gamma = (\mu_\gamma^{\mathrm{I}} - \mu_\gamma^{\mathrm{II}}) + z_\gamma \mathfrak{F}(\varphi^{\mathrm{I}} - \varphi^{\mathrm{II}}) \qquad (5.28)$$

More simply

$$\tilde{A}_\gamma = \Delta\mu_\gamma + z_\gamma \mathfrak{F}\Delta\varphi \qquad (5.29)$$

where Δ denotes the difference in the value of a given variable between vessel I and vessel II. Temperature and composition being the same in both vessels, we have (cf., second formula (3.21))

$$\Delta\mu_\gamma = v_\gamma \Delta p \qquad (5.29')$$

where v_γ is the specific molar volume of constituent γ. (5.27) can thus be written in the more explicit form

$$\frac{d_iS}{dt} = -\frac{1}{T}\sum_\gamma v_\gamma \frac{dn_\gamma^{\mathrm{I}}}{dt}\Delta p - \frac{1}{T}\sum_\gamma z_\gamma \mathfrak{F}\frac{dn_\gamma^{\mathrm{I}}}{dt}\Delta\varphi \qquad (5.30)$$

We introduce the fluxes

$$J = -\sum_\gamma v_\gamma \frac{dn_\gamma^{\mathrm{I}}}{dt}; \qquad I = -\sum_\gamma z_\gamma \mathfrak{F}\frac{dn_\gamma^{\mathrm{I}}}{dt} \qquad (5.31)$$

where I is the electrical current, due to a transfer of charges from I to II, and J the resultant flow of matter (J might also be called a resultant flow of "volume"). The entropy production (5.28) now becomes

$$\frac{d_iS}{dt} = \frac{J\Delta p}{T} + \frac{I\Delta\varphi}{T} \qquad (5.32)$$

and the phenomenological equations are given by

$$\left.\begin{aligned} I &= L_{11} \frac{\Delta \varphi}{T} + L_{12} \frac{\Delta p}{T} \\ J &= L_{21} \frac{\Delta \varphi}{T} + L_{22} \frac{\Delta p}{T} \end{aligned}\right\} \tag{5.33}$$

with the Onsager relation

$$L_{12} = L_{21} \tag{5.34}$$

We have here two irreversible effects, transport of matter under the influence of a difference of pressure and electrical current due to the difference of electrical potential. Moreover, we have a cross effect related by the coefficient $L_{12} = L_{21}$, which is due to the interference of the two irreversible processes.

We now turn to the definition of the electrokinetic effects. In the first place, we have the *streaming potential* defined as the potential difference per unit pressure difference in the state with zero electrical current. From (5.33) we get

$$\left(\frac{\Delta \varphi}{\Delta p}\right)_{I=0} = -\frac{L_{12}}{L_{11}} \qquad \text{(streaming potential)} \tag{5.35}$$

The second electrokinetic effect is called *electro-osmosis* and is defined as the flow of matter per unit electrical current in the state with uniform pressure. Using again (5.33) it follows that

$$\left(\frac{J}{I}\right)_{\Delta p=0} = \frac{L_{21}}{L_{11}} \qquad \text{(electro-osmosis)} \tag{5.36}$$

The third effect is called *electro-osmotic pressure* and is defined as the pressure difference per unit potential difference when the flow J is zero,

$$\left(\frac{\Delta p}{\Delta \varphi}\right)_{J=0} = -\frac{L_{21}}{L_{22}} \qquad \text{(electro-osmotic pressure)} \tag{5.37}$$

The fourth effect is the *streaming current*

$$\left(\frac{I}{J}\right)_{\Delta\varphi=0} = \frac{L_{12}}{L_{22}} \qquad \text{(streaming current)} \tag{5.38}$$

Between these four effects which can be studied experimentally, independently, the Onsager relation gives the two connections

$$\left(\frac{\Delta\varphi}{\Delta p}\right)_{I=0} = -\left(\frac{J}{I}\right)_{\Delta p=0} \tag{5.39}$$

$$\left(\frac{\Delta p}{\Delta\varphi}\right)_{J=0} = -\left(\frac{I}{J}\right)_{\Delta\varphi=0} \tag{5.40}$$

These two relations both relate an osmotic effect to a streaming effect. Relation (5.39), known as Saxen's relation, had already been established by applying kinetic considerations. However, such kinetic considerations are only possible if some simplified model of the diaphragm separating the two phases is adopted, for example, if the diaphragm is identified with a capillary of uniform section. The importance of the thermodynamic demonstration resides in the fact that it holds, whatever the nature of the diaphragm or the porous wall. This example is instructive in that it shows clearly what kind of information can be obtained from the thermodynamics of irreversible processes. Although such methods are insufficient for the explicit calculation of the thermodynamic coefficients, they make it possible to establish a connection between effects which at first sight appear to be quite independent. The situation is the same as in the thermodynamics of equilibria, where thermodynamic methods permit us to connect macroscopic phenomena such as osmotic pressure and vapor pressure.

3. Thermomolecular Pressure Difference and Thermomechanical Effect

As a second example, we shall again consider a system composed of two vessels I and II, which communicate by means of a capillary, a small hole, a membrane or a porous wall. A temperature difference is now maintained between the two vessels. For convenience, we shall limit ourselves to the case of a one-component system and we shall ignore electrical processes. The entropy production for such a system has already been calculated (cf., 3.53). We may use the fluxes and affinities of the form given by (4.16)–(4.20), and we shall use the same notation as in these equations but drop for convenience the dash in the X and the J. For a one-component system the affinities are given by (cf., 3.21)

$$X_{\text{th}} = \Delta\left(\frac{1}{T}\right) = -\frac{1}{T^2}\,\Delta T \tag{5.41}$$

$$X_m = -\frac{(\Delta\mu)_T}{T} = -\frac{v}{T}\,\Delta p \tag{5.42}$$

And the fluxes of energy and matter by

$$J_{\text{th}} = \frac{d_i^{\text{II}}\Phi}{dt} - h\,\frac{dn^{\text{II}}}{dt} \tag{5.43}$$

$$J_m = \frac{dn^{\text{II}}}{dt} \tag{5.44}$$

The entropy production becomes

$$\frac{d_iS}{dt} = -J_{\text{th}}\,\frac{1}{T^2}\,\Delta T - J_m\,\frac{v}{T}\,\Delta p \tag{5.45}$$

and the phenomenological laws now read

$$\begin{aligned} J_{\text{th}} &= -L_{11}\,\frac{\Delta T}{T^2} - L_{12}\,\frac{v\Delta p}{T} \\ J_m &= -L_{21}\,\frac{\Delta T}{T^2} - L_{22}\,\frac{v\Delta p}{T} \end{aligned} \tag{5.46}$$

we have again the Onsager relation

$$L_{12} = L_{21} \tag{5.47}$$

The first phenomenon we have to study is the *thermomolecular pressure* difference defined as the differences of pressure which arise between the two phases in the stationary state $J_m = 0$, when a temperature difference is maintained. According to (5.46) this pressure difference is given by

$$\left(\frac{\Delta p}{\Delta T}\right)_{J_m=0} = -\frac{L_{21}}{L_{22}vT}$$

(Thermomolecular pressure difference) (5.48)

This is a cross-phenomenon due to the interference of the irreversible processes of transport of energy and matter. In the stationary state ($J_m = 0$), the state variables of the system no longer depend on the variable time although it is clear that this is not an equilibrium state, since the flux J_{th} and the corresponding entropy production (5.45) are different from zero. We shall study such stationary nonequilibrium states in greater detail in the next chapter.

The thermomolecular pressure difference appears when the system consists of a gas and the vessels are separated by narrow capillaries or small openings. It is then called the "*Knudsen effect*" and it will be studied in the next section from the kinetic point of view. The thermomolecular pressure difference occurs also in liquid helium below the λ point (2.19°K), where it is then called the "*fountain effect.*"

When the same effect manifests itself in gases or liquids with a membrane separating two phases, it is called "*thermo-osmosis*" [41, 42]. In this case the sign of Δp for a given value of ΔT depends essentially on the nature of the membrane.

We now turn our attention to the second effect which occurs in the system defined at the beginning of this section. If we maintain a certain pressure difference between the two vessels and a uniform temperature throughout the system, matter flows fron one vessel to the other and an associated energy flow proportional to flow of matter is observed. The energy flow can be measured by determining the heat which is necessary to maintain a uniform temperature in the system. This effect is called the "*thermomechanical effect*" and it can be expressed in terms of the phenomenological coefficients (cf., 5.46)

$$\left(\frac{J_{\mathrm{th}}}{J_m}\right)_{\Delta T=0} = \frac{L_{12}}{L_{22}} \quad \text{(thermomechanical effect)} \qquad (5.49)$$

The quantity L_{12}/L_{22} has the physical significance of an energy transfer per unit transfer of mass. It is often called the *heat of transfer*

$$Q^* = \frac{L_{12}}{L_{22}} \qquad (5.50)$$

Onsager's reciprocity relation (5.47) establishes the relation between the thermomolecular pressure difference and the thermomechanical effect

$$\left(\frac{\Delta p}{\Delta T}\right)_{J_m=0} = -\frac{1}{vT}\left(\frac{J_{\mathrm{th}}}{J_m}\right)_{\Delta T=0} \qquad (5.51)$$

It is thus clear that both effects will appear in the same system. In fact, the thermomechanical effect has been observed in a Knudsen gas and in liquid helium below the λ point.

As both effects depend on the value of the heat of transfer Q^*, it is of interest to gain further insight into the physical significance of this heat of transfer. The principle of conservation of energy (2.13), when applied to phase II, leads to

$$\frac{dE^{\text{II}}}{dt} = \frac{d^{\text{II}}\Phi}{dt} \tag{5.52}$$

Splitting $d^{\text{II}}\Phi$ into the part received from the exterior $d_e^{\text{II}}Q$ and the contribution from phase I (cf., 2.21) and taking account of (5.42), (5.44), (5.49), and (5.50), we obtain

$$\frac{dE^{\text{II}}}{dt} = \frac{d_e^{\text{II}}Q}{dt} + (Q^* + h)\frac{dn^{\text{II}}}{dt} \tag{5.53}$$

It can thus be seen that $Q^* + h$ is the average energy transferred to phase II per unit mass transfer and we will denote it by e^*. The relation

$$e^* = Q^* + h$$

or

$$Q^* = e^* - h \tag{5.54}$$

opens the way to a kinetic evaluation of the heat of transfer as we shall see in the next section.

4. Kinetic Interpretation of Heat of Transfer—Knudsen Gas

In the case of the Knudsen gas, that is, when the two phases communicate by an opening, the diameter of which is small compared to the mean free path, it is quite simple to calculate directly the thermomolecular pressure difference. It may be safely assumed that every molecule which arrives at the opening will pass freely through it. According to the basic formulae of the kinetic theory of gases, the number of molecules coming from phase I, which pass through the opening is proportional to $p^{\text{I}}/\sqrt{T^{\text{I}}}$; similarly, the coresponding number of molecules from phase II is proportionnal to $p^{\text{II}}/\sqrt{T^{\text{II}}}$. For the stationary state, in which the resultant flow of matter is zero, we then have

$$\frac{p^{\mathrm{I}}}{p^{\mathrm{II}}} = \sqrt{\frac{T^{\mathrm{I}}}{T^{\mathrm{II}}}} \tag{5.55}$$

This is Knudsen's relationship for the thermomolecular pressure difference.* In differential form, the relation should be written as

$$\frac{\Delta p}{\Delta T} = \frac{1}{2}\frac{p}{T} = \frac{R}{2v} \tag{5.56}$$

The value of the heat of transfer for a Knudsen gas is obtained by comparison with (5.48) and (5.50)

$$Q^* = -\frac{RT}{2} \tag{5.57}$$

It is also possible to obtain this value of the heat of transfer by direct statistical computation, using relation (5.54). We can thus calculate the mean energy e^* transported by a molecule crossing the opening. Let us take the direction of the x coordinate perpendicular to the opening and denote by v_x the x component of the velocity of a molecule and by f the corresponding velocity distribution function. It is well known that f is proportional (Maxwell's distribution law) to

$$\exp - \frac{mv_x^2}{2kT} \tag{5.58}$$

The total flow of molecules through the unit area of the opening per unit time is given by

$$C\bar{v}_x = \int_0^\infty fv_x dv_x \tag{5.59}$$

Each molecule transports a kinetic energy $\frac{1}{2}mv^2 = \frac{1}{2}mv_x^2 + \frac{1}{2}mv_y^2 + \frac{1}{2}mv_z^2$. We first calculate the mean

* For an example of the experimental verification of (5.55) with gaseous helium, cf. Weber and Schmidt [43].

value of $\frac{1}{2}\, mv_x^2$ for the molecules which cross the opening. The total flow of energy (per unit time and unit area of the opening) corresponding to the coordinate x is simply

$$C\overline{\frac{1}{2}\, mv_x^2 \cdot v_x} = \frac{m}{2}\int_0^\infty f v_x^3\, dv_x \tag{5.60}$$

The mean value of the energy, $\frac{1}{2}\, mv_x^2$, transported per molecule is given by the ratio of the total flow of energy to the total flow of molecules and may be evaluated by the standard methods of integration

$$\frac{m}{2}\frac{\int_0^\infty f v_x^3 dv_x}{\int_0^\infty f v_x dv_x} = kT \tag{5.61}$$

This is exactly twice the equipartition value $\frac{1}{2}\, kT$ and is a direct consequence of the fact that molecules with high velocities have a greater chance of crossing the opening than slow molecules.

The mean values of $\frac{1}{2}\, mv_y^2$ and $\frac{1}{2}\, mv_z^2$ are given simply by the equipartition value $\frac{1}{2}\, kT$, so that we obtain for the mean total energy of transfer, *per mole*

$$e^* = 2RT \tag{5.62}$$

The heat of transfer, as given by (5.54), is

$$Q^* = 2RT - (5/2)RT = -\frac{RT}{2} \tag{5.63}$$

in agreement with (5.57).

It can be shown that the preceding kinetic argument may be adapted to the case of membranes [42].

In all cases in which the mean energy of the molecules crossing the separating layer between the two phases is different from the enthalpy h, we have a heat of transfer and also a thermomolecular pressure difference and a thermomechanical effect. It is clear that in some respects the separation layer acts as a sieve, favoring the crossing of some kinds of molecules as, for example, molecules with high energies.

If the two phases are separated by an opening wide enough for the gas to move through it in bulk, e will contain the work term pv besides the specific energy e and

$$e^* = e + pv = h, \qquad Q^* = e^* - h = 0 \tag{5.64}$$

so that the heat of transfer is zero. The intermediate case has been studied thoroughly by S. Weber (cf. for a review in the case of helium, W. H. Keesom [44]) but no simple formulae can be derived. The value of the heat of transfer depends on the ratio of the mean free path and the dimensions of the hole or the capillary which separates the two phases.

5. Diffusion—Einstein's Relation

This section will be devoted to a brief discussion of two diffusion problems. Our starting point is the relation (3.75). The corresponding phenomenological law is given by

$$\rho_1(\omega_1 - \omega_2) = \frac{L}{T}\left(\mathfrak{F}_1 - \frac{\partial \overset{+}{\mu_1}}{\partial x}\right) \tag{5.65}$$

For a perfect gas or a dilute solution, the chemical potential is of the form (cf. Chapter III, § 5)

$$\mu_1 = \eta_1(T) + RT \log C_1 \tag{5.66}$$

and this gives for (5.65)

$$C_1(\omega_1 - \omega_2) = \frac{L}{T}\left(\mathfrak{F}_1 M_1 - \frac{\partial \mu_1}{\partial x}\right) = -\frac{L}{T}\frac{RT}{C_1}\left(\frac{\partial C_1}{\partial x} - \frac{\mathfrak{F}_1 M_1 C_1}{RT}\right) \tag{5.67}$$

We shall consider two particular cases. For a *uniform system*,

$$(\omega_1 - \omega_2) = \frac{L}{TC_1} \mathfrak{F}_1 M_1 \tag{5.68}$$

the coefficient of proportionality between the relative velocity $\omega_1 - \omega_2$ and the force $\mathfrak{F}_1 M_1$ (per mole),

$$B = \frac{L}{TC_1} \tag{5.69}$$

is called the *mobility* of component 1.

The second case refers to a system without external forces

$$C_1(\omega_1 - \omega_2) = -\frac{L}{T}\frac{RT}{C_1}\frac{\partial C_1}{\partial x} \tag{5.70}$$

The coefficient of proportionality between the flux of diffusion $C_1\ (\omega_1 - \omega_2)$ and the concentration gradient is, by definition, the *diffusion coefficient*

$$D = \frac{L}{T}\frac{RT}{C_1} \tag{5.71}$$

Comparing (5.69) and (5.71) we obtain the Einstein relation between mobility and diffusion coefficients

$$D = RTB \tag{5.72}$$

This relation is quite general and has been derived without making any special kinetic assumptions.

As a second example, we shall examine the general definition of the diffusion coefficient. For a system without external forces, (5.65) can be written in the form

$$C_1(\omega_1 - \omega_2) = -\frac{L}{T}\frac{\partial \mu_1}{\partial N_1}\frac{\partial N_1}{\partial x} \tag{5.73}$$

From the phenomenological point of view, the diffusion coefficient D is defined by

$$C_1(\omega_1 - \omega_2) = -DC \frac{\partial N_1}{\partial x} \tag{5.74}$$

so that

$$D = \frac{1}{TC} L \frac{\partial \mu_1}{\partial N_1} \tag{5.75}$$

For a perfect gas or a dilute solution this definition is equivalent to (5.71). The diffusion coefficient is the product of the phenomenological coefficient L and the thermodynamic quantity $(1/TC)(\partial\mu_1/\partial N_1)$. The coefficient L is always positive, and so is the quantity $\partial\mu_1/\partial N_1$ for all ideal systems (perfect gases, ideal solutions . . .). It then results from (5.75) that the diffusion coefficient is positive and according to (5.74) the flow of diffusion is directed in a direction such that existing concentration/gradients are compensated. In some systems such as in the system containing two "non-miscible" liquids like benzene and water, it may occur that $\partial\mu_1/\partial N_1$ is negative. In this case the liquids form two phases, one rich in the first component and the other in the second. For such a pair of liquids the diffusion coefficient is negative in the zone of demixtion corresponding to thermodynamic instability [9a]. The possibility of negative diffusion coefficients in contrast to the thermal conductivity, which is always positive, results from the fact that the diffusion coefficient is a productof two functions of which only one has a definite sign.

Many other applications of thermodynamical methods to diffusion have been treated but we cannot go into further details here (see especially [18, 45, 46]).

6. Continuous and Discontinuous Formalism

Let us finally indicate a method which permits us to move easily from the "discontinuous formalism" which we generally use in this book to the case of continuous systems as defined in Chapter III, § 10.

We consider the simple case of thermal conductivity. The entropy production is then given by the formula (see 5.1)

$$d_iS/dt = \int \sigma dV = -\int (W_x/T^2)(\partial T/\partial x)dV \qquad (5.76)$$

We may put this equation into a form identical to (4.1). In order to do so, we develop W and T in Fourier series (we suppress the index x of W, as well as the volume factors which appear as normalization factors in 5.77 and 5.78)

$$W = \sum_f W_f \exp(ifx) \qquad T = \sum_f T_f \exp(ifx) \qquad (5.77)$$

Let us introduce these expansions into (5.76). We then find, neglecting higher order terms (T_o means T_f for $f = 0$)

$$d_iS/dT = 1/T_o^2 \sum_{ff'} T_f if W_{f'} \int \exp[i(f + f')x]dx \qquad (5.78)$$

$$= -1/T_o^2 \sum_f if T_f W_{-f}$$

This expression is the exact analog of (4.1). Here the fluxes J_i are the Fourier components of W, and the generalized forces are ifT_f. Starting with this expression for the entropy we may proceed exactly as we did for discontinuous systems. For example, the Fourier law (5.2), (5.3) becomes

$$W_f = -if\lambda T_f \qquad (5.79)$$

Again, this expression is the exact analog of the linear laws for discontinuous systems.

CHAPTER VI

Stationary Non-equilibrium States

1. Thermodynamic Significance of Stationary Non-equilibrium States

In Section 3, Chapter V, we met a typical stationary nonequilibrium state in dealing with thermomolecular pressure differences. In this state, the transport of matter J_m is zero, yet the transport of energy between the two phases at different temperatures as well as the entropy production are different from zero. By contrast, the state variables no longer depend on time so that this state may be well described as a stationary non-equilibrium state or more briefly as a stationary state. No confusion should arise between such states and equilibrium states which are characterized by zero entropy production. Another example of a stationary state is afforded by a system which receives a component M from the outside environment and transforms it through a certain number of intermediate compounds into a final product F which is returned to the external environment. A stationary state arises when the concentrations of the intermediate components no longer vary with time. In this case the conditions for the occurrence of a stationary state are expressed by some relations between the reaction rates of the different processes which correspond to the formation or the destruction of the intermediate compounds.

We shall see that stationary states may be characterized by an extremum principle which states that in the stationary state, the entropy production has its minimum value compatible with some auxiliary conditions to be specified in each case.

In our first example (thermomolecular pressure difference) the condition imposed is the difference of temperature between the phases I and II. In the second example, the conditions imposed may be the values of the concentrations of the initial and final products A and F in the external environment.

The question of which variable it is that characterizes stationary states has been often discussed, both by physicists (P. and T. Ehrenfest [47], Rutgers [48], Zwicky [49], and by biologists (Lotka [50], Hearon [51]). The answer to this question is given by the thermodynamics of irreversible processes [17, 18, 52, 53].

2. States of Minimum Entropy Production

Consider entropy production as corresponding to a transfer of matter and energy between two phases at different temperatures. This entropy production per unit time is given by (cf., 5.45)

$$\frac{d_iS}{dt} = J_{\text{th}}X_{\text{th}} + J_mX_m > 0 \tag{6.1}$$

and the phenomenological laws are (cf., 5.46)

$$\left.\begin{aligned} J_{\text{th}} &= L_{11}X_{\text{th}} + L_{12}X_m \\ J_m &= L_{21}X_{\text{th}} + L_{22}X_m \end{aligned}\right\} \tag{6.2}$$

For the stationary state

$$J_m = L_{21}X_{\text{th}} + L_{22}X_m = 0 \tag{6.3}$$

We shall now derive (6.3) as the condition that the entropy production is minimum for a given value of X_{th}. Using (6.2) and Onsager's reciprocity relation $L_{12} = L_{21}$, the entropy production (6.1) becomes

$$\frac{d_iS}{dt} = L_{11}X^2_{\text{th}} + 2L_{21}X_{\text{th}}X_m + L_{22}X^2_m > 0 \qquad (6.4)$$

Taking the derivative of (6.4) with respect to X_m, at constant X_{th}, we have

$$\frac{\partial}{\partial X_m}\left(\frac{d_iS}{dt}\right) = 2(L_{21}X_{\text{th}} + L_{22}X_m) = 2J_m = 0 \qquad (6.5)$$

The two conditions

$$J_m = 0 \qquad \text{or} \qquad \frac{\partial}{\partial X_m}\left(\frac{d_iS}{dt}\right) = 0 \qquad (6.6)$$

are completely equivalent as long as the linear relations (6.2) are valid.

This argument can be generalized immediately to the case of n independent affinities $X_1 \ldots X_n$ of which a certain number k, $X_1 \ldots X_k$ are kept constant. For the stationary state we then have

$$J_{k+1} = \ldots = J_n = 0 \qquad (6.7)$$

These conditions are equivalent to the minimum conditions for entropy production

$$\frac{\partial}{\partial X_j}\left(\frac{d_iS}{dt}\right) = 0 \qquad (j = k + 1, \ldots, n) \qquad (6.8)$$

Let us notice also that as d_iS/dt is a definite positive quadratic expression, the extremum condition defined by (6.8) refers to a minimum.

In the next section, we shall deal with an example of stationary states corresponding to fixed values of some linear combinations of the affinities.

3. Consecutive Chemical Reactions

Consider an open system which undergoes a sequence of consecutive reactions which we shall write down in the form

$$\begin{array}{ll} M \rightarrow N & (1) \\ N \rightarrow O & (2) \\ \cdot & \\ \cdot & \\ \cdot & \\ \cdot & \\ P \rightarrow F & (r) \end{array} \tag{6.9}$$

Only the components M and F can be exchanged with the external environment, so that (cf. 1.8)

$$\frac{dn_M}{dt} = \frac{d_e n_M}{dt} - \mathrm{v}_1; \frac{dn_N}{dt} = \mathrm{v}_1 - \mathrm{v}_2; \qquad \frac{dn_F}{dt} = \frac{d_e n_F}{dt} + \mathrm{v}_r \tag{6.10}$$

For the stationary state

$$\frac{d_e n_M}{dt} = \mathrm{v}_1 = \mathrm{v}_2 = \ldots = \mathrm{v}_r = -\frac{d_e n_F}{dt} \tag{6.11}$$

The entropy production including the two transport processes

M (outside world) $\rightarrow$ M (system)

F (outside world) $\rightarrow$ F (system)

is given by

$$T\frac{d_i S}{dt} = A_M \frac{d_e n_M}{dt} + \sum_{\rho=1}^{r} A_\rho \mathrm{v}_\rho + A_F \frac{d_e n_F}{dt} > 0 \tag{6.12}$$

where A_M and A_F are the affinities corresponding to the transport of components M and F, and A_ρ is the affinity of the ρth reaction (6.9).

If we denote the system itself by I and the external environment by II, then (cf., 3.27)

$$A_M = \mu_M^{\mathrm{I}} - \mu_M^{\mathrm{II}}; \qquad A_F = \mu_F^{\mathrm{I}} - \mu_F^{\mathrm{II}} \tag{6.12'}$$

In the stationary state (6.11)

$$T\frac{d_i S}{dt} = (A_M + \sum_\rho A_\rho - A_F)\mathrm{v} = A\mathrm{v} > 0 \tag{6.13}$$

where v is the common value of all the partial rates (6.11) and A is the resultant affinity

$$A = A_M + \sum_\rho A_\rho - A_F \tag{6.14}$$

corresponding to the global process

$$M \text{ (external environment)} \rightarrow F \text{ (external environment)} \tag{6.15}$$

This affinity, which may often be written in the simple form (cf. 5.11)

$$A = RT \log \frac{K(T)}{C_M^{-1} C_F} \tag{6.16}$$

depends essentially on the concentrations C_M and C_F in the outside environment. It is now quite easy to show that relations (6.11) are precisely the conditions of minimum entropy production for a *given value of the resultant affinity*. Using the phenomenological linear laws, (6.12) may be expressed as a quadratic form in the affinities

$$\frac{d_iS}{dt} = \sum_{\rho=1}^{r+2} \sum_{\rho'=1}^{r+2} L_{\rho\rho'} \frac{A_\rho}{T} \frac{A_{\rho'}}{T} > 0 \tag{6.17}$$

The summation in (6.17) extends over the $r + 2$ irreversible processes which appear in (6.12).

We now have to determine the minimum value of (6.17) for a given value of the resultant affinity (6.14). This may be done by the method of Lagrange's undetermined multipliers which takes account of condition (6.14) by determining the extremum of the function

$$\Phi = \sum_\rho \sum_{\rho'} L_{\rho\rho'} \frac{A_\rho}{T} \frac{A_{\rho'}}{T} - 2\lambda \sum_\rho \frac{A_\rho}{T} \tag{6.18}$$

where λ is the Lagrange multiplier. The extremum conditions of (6.18) are thus given by

$$\frac{\partial \Phi}{\partial (A_\rho/T)} = 2 \sum_{\rho'} L_{\rho\rho'} \frac{A_{\rho'}}{T} - 2\lambda = 0 \tag{6.19}$$

or
$$v_\rho = \lambda \qquad (\rho = 1,2 \ldots r + 2), \tag{6.20}$$
which are precisely our stationary conditions (6.11).

4. More Complicated Systems of Chemical Reactions

The considerations of the preceding section can readily be extended to the case of a more complicated system of chemical reactions. As an example we consider the synthesis of hydrobromic acid [54]

$$\begin{aligned} Br_2 &\rightarrow 2Br & (1)\\ Br + H_2 &\rightarrow HBr + H & (2)\\ Br_2 + H &\rightarrow HBr + Br & (3) \end{aligned} \tag{6.21}$$

The macroscopic stoichiometric equation is

$$Br_2 + H_2 \rightarrow 2HBr \qquad (2) + (3) \tag{6.22}$$

Reaction (1) does not appear in (6.22). If, for convenience, we ignore the affinities of transport processes, the stationary state now corresponds to an extremum of entropy production for a given value of the resultant affinity (cf. 6.14)

$$A = A_2 + A_3 \tag{6.23}$$

Instead of (6.20), it is then found that the extremum conditions of entropy production are given by

$$v_1 = 0 \qquad v_2 = v_3 \tag{6.24}$$

It is clear that then the time variation of the concentrations inside the system is zero

$$\left.\begin{aligned} \frac{dn_H}{dt} &= v_2 - v_3 = 0\\ \frac{dn_{Br}}{dt} &= 2v_1 - v_2 + v_3 = 0 \end{aligned}\right\} \tag{6.25}$$

Here again the stationary conditions are equivalent to the conditions of minimum production of entropy.

5. Time Variation of Entropy Production—Stability of Stationary States

We shall now study in greater detail the time variation of entropy production and we shall prove that irreversible processes taking place inside a thermodynamic system always lower the value of the entropy production per unit time. For the entropy production per unit time we shall use the following notation

$$\mathcal{P} \equiv \frac{d_i S}{dt} \tag{6.26}$$

For convenience, we consider the case of a system which undergoes only two simultaneous chemical changes although the argument can be easily extended to the general case. The entropy production per unit time is as usual (cf. 6.4)

$$\mathcal{P} = L_{11}\left(\frac{A_1}{T}\right)^2 + 2L_{12}\frac{A_1 A_2}{T^2} + L_{22}\left(\frac{A_2}{T}\right)^2 > 0 \tag{6.27}$$

We still suppose that the phenomenological coefficients L_{ij} are constant in time. We then have

$$\frac{1}{2}\frac{d\mathcal{P}}{dt} = \left(L_{11}\frac{A_1}{T} + L_{12}\frac{A_2}{T}\right)\frac{d(A_1/T)}{dt} + \left(L_{12}\frac{A_1}{T} + L_{22}\frac{A_2}{T}\right)\frac{d\,(A_2/T)}{dt}$$

$$= \mathrm{v}_1\frac{d\,(A_1/T)}{dt} + \mathrm{v}_2\frac{d\,(A_2/T)}{dt} \tag{6.28}$$

Let us first consider a *closed system.* A_1 and A_2 may then be expressed in terms of two independent physical variables (for example p and T), which we shall assume to be constant, and ξ_1, ξ_2, so that

$$\frac{1}{2}\frac{d\mathcal{P}}{dt} = \frac{\mathrm{v}_1}{T}\left[\left(\frac{\partial A_1}{\partial \xi_1}\right)_{pT}\mathrm{v}_1 + \left(\frac{\partial A_1}{\partial \xi_2}\right)_{pT}\mathrm{v}_2\right] +$$

$$\frac{\mathrm{v}_2}{T}\left[\left(\frac{\partial A_2}{\partial \xi_1}\right)_{pT}\mathrm{v}_1 + \left(\frac{\partial A_2}{\partial \xi_2}\right)_{pT}\mathrm{v}_2\right] \tag{6.29}$$

As we know that (cf. 3.44)

$$\left(\frac{\partial A_1}{\partial \xi_2}\right)_{pT} = \left(\frac{\partial A_2}{\partial \xi_1}\right)_{pT} = -\left(\frac{\partial^2 G}{\partial \xi_1 \partial \xi_2}\right)_{pT} \tag{6.30}$$

(6.29) may be written in the form

$$\frac{1}{2}\frac{d\mathcal{P}}{dt} = \frac{1}{T}\left(\frac{\partial A_1}{\partial \xi_1} \mathrm{v}_1^2 + 2\,\frac{\partial A_1}{\partial \xi_2}\,\mathrm{v}_1\mathrm{v}_2 + \frac{\partial A_2}{\partial \xi_2}\mathrm{v}_2^2\right) < 0 \tag{6.31}$$

We recall that in considering fluctuations (Chapter IV, § 3), we have already seen (cf., 4.28) that $\partial A_\rho/\partial \xi_{\rho'}$ are the coefficients of a definite negative quadratic form. It is therefore evident that in a closed system the entropy production per unit time can only diminish with time.

This argument can readily be extended to *open systems.** The affinities are then functions of the mole numbers $n_1 \ldots n_c$. Using (1.8) we have

$$\begin{aligned}
\frac{dA_1}{dt} &= \sum_\gamma \frac{\partial A_1}{\partial n_\gamma}\frac{dn_\gamma}{dt} = \sum_\gamma \frac{\partial A_1}{\partial n_\gamma}\frac{d_i n_\gamma}{dt} + \sum_\gamma \frac{\partial A_1}{\partial n_\gamma}\frac{d_e n_\gamma}{dt} \\
&= \sum_\gamma \frac{\partial A_1}{\partial n_\gamma}\nu_{\gamma 1}\frac{d\xi_1}{dt} + \sum_\gamma \frac{\partial A_1}{\partial n_\gamma}\nu_{\gamma 2}\frac{d\xi_2}{dt} + \sum_\gamma \frac{\partial A_1}{\partial n_\gamma}\frac{d_e n_\gamma}{dt} \\
&= \frac{\partial A_1}{\partial \xi_1}\mathrm{v}_1 + \frac{\partial A_1}{\partial \xi_2}\mathrm{v}_2 + \sum_\gamma \frac{\partial A_1}{\partial n_\gamma}\frac{d_e n_\gamma}{dt}
\end{aligned} \tag{6.32}$$

Using this relation in (6.28), we find

$$\begin{aligned}
\frac{1}{2}\frac{d\mathcal{P}}{dt} = \frac{1}{T}\left(\frac{\partial A_1}{\partial \xi_1}\mathrm{v}_1^2 + 2\,\frac{\partial A_1}{\partial \xi_2}\mathrm{v}_1\mathrm{v}_2 + \frac{\partial A_2}{\partial \xi_2}\,\mathrm{v}_2^2\right) \\
+ \frac{1}{T}\sum_\gamma\left(\mathrm{v}_1\frac{\partial A_1}{\partial n_\gamma} + \mathrm{v}_2\frac{\partial A_2}{\partial n_\gamma}\right)\frac{d_e n_\gamma}{dt}
\end{aligned} \tag{6.33}$$

The time variation of the entropy production per unit time can be split into two terms: an internal term which is always negative

---

* Here the entropy production (6.26) does not include the transport processes, contrary to the treatment used in § 3 of this chapter. If the transport processes are included in (6.26), the entropy production always decreases on time. We shall come back to the time variation of the entropy production in the Appendix.

$$\frac{1}{2}\frac{d_i\mathcal{P}}{dt} = \frac{1}{T}\left(\frac{\partial A_1}{\partial \xi_1} v_1^2 + 2\frac{\partial A_1}{\partial \xi_2} v_1 v_2 + \frac{\partial A_2}{\partial \xi_2} v_2^2\right) < 0 \qquad (6.34)$$

and an external term with no definite sign

$$\frac{1}{2}\frac{d_e\mathcal{P}}{dt} = \frac{1}{T}\sum_\gamma \left(v_1\frac{\partial A_1}{\partial n_\gamma} + v_2\frac{\partial A_2}{\partial n_\gamma}\right)\frac{d_e n_\gamma}{dt} \qquad (6.35)$$

We may conclude that the internal irreversible processes always operate in such a way that their effect is to lower the value of the entropy production per unit time. This result has an immediate bearing on the stability of stationary states. When a system is in a state of minimum entropy production then, according to inequality (6.34), it cannot leave this state by a spontaneous irreversible change. If, as a result of some fluctuation, it deviates slightly from this state, internal changes will take place and bring back the system to its initial state, which may be referred to as a *stable state;* the transformations which occur in such a state may be called *stable transformations.*

The problem of the stability of stationary states can also be studied by means of an extension of the so-called Le Chatelier principle of moderation. This alternative method may be found elsewhere [17, 18].

6. Entropy Flow in Stationary States

In the stationary states all state variables are independent of time and this is also true for the entropy. It is clear that a positive entropy production has to be compensated by a negative flow of entropy in such a way that the total time variation of entropy is zero

$$\frac{dS}{dt} = \frac{d_eS}{dt} + \frac{d_iS}{dt} = 0 \qquad (6.36)$$

As

$$\frac{d_iS}{dt} > 0 \qquad (6.37)$$

we necessarily have that

$$\frac{d_eS}{dt} < 0 \tag{6.38}$$

Stationary non-equilibrium states *cannot occur in isolated systems* for a flow of entropy is necessary to maintain the stationary state. As an example, we shall again consider the system studied in Chapter III § 8 and recall that it is formed by two phases at temperature T^{I} and T^{II}. Both phases individually are open systems, but the system as a whole is closed. The entropy flow is given by (3.51)

$$\frac{d_eS}{dt} = \frac{1}{T^{\mathrm{I}}}\frac{d_e^{\mathrm{I}}Q}{dt} + \frac{1}{T^{\mathrm{II}}}\frac{d_e^{\mathrm{II}}Q}{dt} \tag{6.39}$$

It is now quite easy to verify the inequality (6.38). Suppose $T^{\mathrm{I}} > T^{\mathrm{II}}$, then $d_e^{\mathrm{I}}Q > 0$, $d_e^{\mathrm{II}}Q < 0$. Moreover, for the stationary state the total heat received by the system is zero

$$dQ = d_e^{\mathrm{I}}Q + d_e^{\mathrm{II}}Q = 0 \tag{6.40}$$

and (6.39) becomes

$$\frac{d_eS}{dt} = \frac{d_e^{\mathrm{I}}Q}{dt}\left(\frac{1}{T^{\mathrm{I}}} - \frac{1}{T^{\mathrm{II}}}\right) < 0 \tag{6.41}$$

The negative entropy flow is here due to the fact that the heat received at temperature T^{I} is returned to the outer world at the lower temperature T^{II}.

As a second example, we shall take an open system. The entropy flow has been given in equation (3.48). Instead of $d\Phi/dt$, which is only defined apart from a term $\beta(dm/dt)$, where β is an arbitrary constant (cf. Chapter II, § 3), it is more convenient to use the flux J'_{th} introduced by (4.16). The entropy flow may then be written as

$$\frac{d_eS}{dt} = \frac{1}{T}J'_{\mathrm{th}} - \sum_{\gamma}\frac{\mu_{\gamma} - h_{\gamma}}{T}\frac{d_en_{\gamma}}{dt}$$

$$= \frac{1}{T} J'_{\text{th}} + \sum_{\gamma} s_{\gamma} \frac{d_e n_{\gamma}}{dt} \tag{6.42}$$

where we have thermodynamic relation between chemical potential μ_{γ}, specific enthalpy h_{γ} and specific entropy s_{γ}

$$\mu_{\gamma} = h_{\gamma} - T s_{\gamma} \tag{6.43}$$

(cf. last formula 3.20 with $G = H - TS$).

The expression (6.42) has to become negative in the stationary state. An interesting limiting case is obtained when $J'_{\text{th}} = 0$, that is, when the entropy exchanges with the external environment are due solely to an exchange of matter. The entropy flow then becomes

$$\frac{d_e S}{dt} = \sum_{\gamma} s_{\gamma} \frac{d_e n_{\gamma}}{dt} \tag{6.44}$$

The inequality (6.38) for the stationary state leads to the conclusion that the entropy of the matter entering the system has to be smaller than the entropy of the matter given off by the system to the external world. From the thermodynamic point of view the open system "degrades" the matter it receives and it is this degradation which maintains the stationary state.

7. Time Variation of the Entropy

In the preceding section, we have seen that entropy flows from a system in a stationary state towards the external environment, thus contributing to the increase of the external entropy. We have also shown that during evolution towards a stationary state the entropy production decreases and takes its lowest value compatible with external constraints when this stationary state is reached.

We shall now examine in greater detail what happens to the entropy of the system during this evolution and shall find that often the entropy itself decreases.

We shall again consider the Knudsen gas (cf. Chapter V, § 4) where we know that the distribution of matter in the stationary state is given by (5.55). We shall now calculate the entropy of the system in the initial uniform state and in the stationary state and thus show that the entropy has decreased during the gradual evolution towards the stationary state. We shall suppose that both phases have the same volume. In the initial state, we have one mole of gas in each phase

$$n_{\text{in}}^{\text{I}} = n_{\text{in}}^{\text{II}} = 1, \qquad n^{\text{I}} + n^{\text{II}} = 2 \tag{6.45}$$

In the stationary state, (5.55) leads to ($V^{\text{I}} = V^{\text{II}} = V$),

$$\frac{n^{\text{I}}}{n^{\text{II}}} = \left(\frac{T^{\text{II}}}{T^{\text{I}}}\right)^{1/2} = \left(1 + \frac{\Delta T}{T}\right)^{1/2} \tag{6.46}$$

Using the second relation (6.45) and (6.46), we find the distribution of matter for the stationary state

$$n_{\text{st}}^{\text{I}} = \frac{2[1 + (\Delta T/T)]^{1/2}}{1 + [1 + (\Delta T/T)]^{1/2}}; \qquad n_{\text{st}}^{\text{II}} = \frac{2}{1 + [1 + (\Delta T/T)]^{1/2}} \tag{6.47}$$

It is shown in textbooks on thermodynamics that the entropy of a perfect gas is given by*

$$S = n\left[\sigma(T) - R \log \frac{n}{V}\right] \tag{6.48}$$

and

$$\frac{\partial S}{\partial T} = n \frac{\partial \sigma}{\partial T} = C_v/T \tag{6.48'}$$

The entropy of our system can thus be written as

$$S = S^{\text{I}} + S^{\text{II}} = n^{\text{I}}\left[\sigma(T) - R \log \frac{n^{\text{I}}}{V}\right] + n^{\text{II}}\left[\sigma(T + \Delta T) - R \log \frac{n^{\text{II}}}{V}\right] \tag{6.49}$$

---

* The symbol σ (T) used in the subsequent formulae (6.48)-(6.50) is not to be confused with the entropy production σ defined in (3.69).

We may apply this formula to the initial state and to the stationary state. It is easily found developing $\sigma(T + \Delta T)$ in powers of $\Delta T/T$, that [17]

$$S_{st} - S_{in} = -\ (1/16)(4C_v + R)\left(\frac{\Delta T}{T}\right)^2 < 0 \quad (6.50)$$

The entropy of the stationary state is smaller than that of the initial state. The same is true for thermal effusion or thermal diffusion. In all these examples the separation of matter which is achieved corresponds to a decrease of entropy in comparison with the initial uniform state.

In other cases however, the entropy increases. This would always be the case for isolated systems if it were not for the fact that such systems cannot be in stationary non-equilibrium states, as we have seen in the preceding section.

8. Stationary State Coupling of Irreversible Processes

So far the interference of irreversible processes has manifested itself only through the existence of interference coefficients L_{ik} $(i \neq k)$ in the phenomenological relations (cf. Chapter IV, § 2). We shall now study some examples of coupling which appears in stationary states between irreversible processes which are not connected directly by phenomenological coefficients, i.e., diffusion and chemical reactions.

Consider an open system (phase I) which receives a component M from the external environment (phase II) and transforms it into a component N, which then is returned to the external environment. Besides M and N, the system also receives some component O which does not take part in the chemical reactions and which we shall call an inert component.

The entropy production due to these irreversible processes is (cf. 6.12 and 6.12′)

$$T\frac{d_iS}{dt} = A_M\frac{d_en_M}{dt} + A_N\frac{d_en_N}{dt} + A_O\frac{d_en_0}{dt} + A_{\text{ch}}\text{v}_{\text{ch}} > 0 \quad (6.51)$$

where A_M, A_N, A_O are the affinities corresponding to the transfer phenomena (cf., 6.12′). We shall assume the following phenomenological relations

$$\left.\begin{aligned} \frac{d_en_M}{dt} &= L_{11}\frac{A_M}{T} + L_{12}\frac{A_0}{T} \\ \frac{d_en_0}{dt} &= L_{21}\frac{A_M}{T} + L_{22}\frac{A_0}{T} \\ \frac{d_en_N}{dt} &= L_N\frac{A_N}{T} \\ \text{v}_{\text{ch}} &= L_{\text{ch}}\frac{A_{\text{ch}}}{T} \end{aligned}\right\} \quad (6.52)$$

For simplicity we have thus assumed that only the transport of components M and O is coupled and we shall examine the consequences of such a coupling in the stationary state. The stationary conditions are

$$\frac{dn_M}{dt} = \frac{d_en_M}{dt} - \text{v}_{\text{ch}} = 0; \quad \frac{dn_N}{dt} = \frac{d_en_N}{dt} + \text{v}_{\text{ch}} = 0;$$

$$\frac{dn_0}{dt} = \frac{d_en_0}{dt} = 0 \quad (6.53)$$

or

$$\text{v}_{\text{ch}} = \frac{d_en_M}{dt} = -\frac{d_en_N}{dt}; \quad \frac{d_en_0}{dt} = 0 \quad (6.54)$$

Using the phenomenological equation (6.52) and Onsager's reciprocity relation ($L_{12} = L_{21}$) we find easily that

$$A_M = \frac{1}{L_{11} - (L_{12}^2/L_{22})} \mathrm{v_{ch}}; \qquad A_N = -\frac{1}{L_N} \mathrm{v_{ch}};$$

$$A_O = \frac{-(L_{21}/L_{22})}{L_{11} - (L_{12}^2/L_{22})} \mathrm{v_{ch}} \quad (6.55)$$

The last formula is very interesting because it shows that in the stationary state a difference of concentration in the inert component O has appeared. Assuming the usual form for the chemical potentials we may write more explicitly (cf. 5.11 and 6.16)

$$A_O = RT \log \frac{K(T)}{(C_O^{\mathrm{II}})^{-1}\,(C_O^{\mathrm{I}})} = -\frac{(L_{21}/L_{22})}{L_{11} - (L_{12}^2/L_{22})} \mathrm{v_{ch}} \quad (6.56)$$

The concentration of O in the open system may be higher or lower than in the medium, according to the algebraic sign of the phenomenological coefficient L_{21}. This effect is proportional to the rate of the chemical reaction. An interference between transport phenomena and chemical reaction may thus appear although the two processes are not directly coupled by the phenomenological laws. We may call such coupling a *stationary coupling.*

As a consequence of the positive value of the entropy production (6.51) in which the rates of the irreversible processes are replaced by their explicit values (6.52) (cf. 4.25), the expression

$$L_{11} - \frac{L_{12}^2}{L_{22}} > 0 \quad (6.57)$$

is always positive, so that the affinity A_{M} has always the same sign as the reaction rate $\mathrm{v_{ch}}$. If component M is effectively consumed by the reaction ($\mathrm{v_{ch}} > 0$), this means that its concentration inside the open system is lowered. But if we assume more general phenomenological laws, this is not always the case. Writing instead of (6.52)

$$\left.\begin{aligned}
\frac{d_e n_M}{dt} &= L_{11}\frac{A_M}{T} + L_{12}\frac{A_O}{T} + L_{13}\frac{A_N}{T} \\
\frac{d_e n_O}{dt} &= L_{21}\frac{A_M}{T} + L_{22}\frac{A_O}{T} + L_{23}\frac{A_N}{T} \\
\frac{d_e n_N}{dt} &= L_{31}\frac{A_M}{T} + L_{32}\frac{A_O}{T} + L_{33}\frac{A_N}{T} \\
\mathrm{v}_{\mathrm{ch}} &= L_{\mathrm{ch}}\frac{A_{\mathrm{ch}}}{T}
\end{aligned}\right\} \tag{6.58}$$

we find instead of (6.56)

$$A_M = \frac{1}{D}\,(L_{22}L_{33} - L_{12}L_{23} - L_{23}^2 + L_{13}L_{22})\mathrm{v}_{\mathrm{ch}} \tag{6.59}$$

where D is the determinant of the L_{ij}

$$D \equiv \begin{vmatrix} L_{11} & L_{12} & L_{13} \\ L_{21} & L_{22} & L_{23} \\ L_{31} & L_{31} & L_{33} \end{vmatrix} > 0 \tag{6.60}$$

As the entropy production (6.51) is positive, the determinant must be positive too, a condition analogous to (4.25). It may happen that the numerator in (6.59) is negative. There would then be in the stationary state a flow of the reacting constituent against its concentration gradient as a result of the stationary state coupling between transport phenomena and chemical reaction.

The importance for biological processes of such a coupling between diffusion and chemical reactions has recently been emphasized by J. Z. Hearon [55] (other examples may be found there). As a consequence of this peculiar situation we may have in a living cell a stationary non-equilibrium distribution of matter which differs from that in the environment by amounts that are determined by the rates of metabolism in the cell.

9. Applications in Biology

The thermodynamics of irreversible processes is almost entirely concerned with the analysis of entropy production and the study of the relations between rates and affinities. Such an analysis is necessary in order to disclose which processes become possible by means of a coupling, that is by use of the *entropy production of another process.*

As an example we may consider the transport of a compound against its concentration gradient. We have seen that this process takes place in different ways which can be classified as follows:

a) Existence of a force which compensates the gradient of the chemical potential (cf. 3.75). This is particularly important for charged particles as the diffusion against a concentration gradient may then be compensated by a difference of electrical potential (cf., Chapter III, § 9).

b) Coupling by means of phenomenological relations. This is the case for the thermomolecular pressure difference (cf., Chapter V, § 3) and, also, in thermodiffusion such a coupling is possible only under certain restrictions (cf., Chapter IV, § 5).

c) Stationary state coupling, as studied in section 8 of this chapter.

A macroscopic classification of this type presents considerable interest when applied to the complicated transport processes occurring in a living organism. It is possible, however, that the irreversible processes related to internal degrees of freedom (cf., Chapter III, § 11) may be important and a more thorough study of this point is highly desirable.

Again, the theory of stationary non-equilibrium states as developed in this chapter may lead to a better understanding of the global behavior of living organisms [56].

We can consider the evolution of the living organism up to the stationary state as taking place under a certain number of constraints determined by the outside world, which are analogous to the parameters that are maintained constant in the examples studied in § 2–4. The exact nature of these constraints can of course only be inferred from a detailed study of the irreversible processes.

The constraints, for example, may be simply the concentrations of some substances in the outside world which are transformed inside the living organism. Whatever the nature of the constant parameters, the stationary state may probably to a good approximation be considered as a state of minimum production of entropy per unit time. This description fits in excellently with some striking characteristics of living organisms. First, the well-known stability against external perturbation has its analogue in the stability of stationary states corresponding to a minimum production of entropy (§ 5). Further, the fact that during growth living organisms actually show a decrease of entropy production during evolution up to the stationary state. Also, the fact that their organization generally increases during this evolution corresponds to the decrease of entropy as studied in § 7. Other arguments may be found in our publication [56]. The behavior of living organisms has always seemed so strange from the point of view of classical thermodynamics that the applicability of thermodynamics to such systems has often been questioned. One may say that from the point of view of the thermodynamics of open and stationary systems a much better understanding of their principal features is obtained.

CHAPTER VII

Non-linear Problems

1. Introduction

The main feature of the thermodynamics of irreversible processes consists of the evaluation of the entropy production and the entropy flow beginning with Gibbs formula (3.17). Such a method must ultimately be justified by the methods of statistical mechanics of irreversible processes. Indeed, the Gibbs formula (3.17) was originally proved for the equilibrium conditions, and its use for the non-equilibrium conditions is a new postulate on which the whole of the thermodynamics of irreversible processes is based. The physical interpretation of this basic formula is that, even without equilibrium, the entropy depends only on the same independent variables as for equilibrium processes. This is certainly not true very far from equilibrium. A detailed comparison between the Gibbs formula and the requirements of the kinetic theory of gases has been made [34]. Space does not permit reproduction of the details here but we would like to quote the results. For transport processes, the domain of validity of the thermodynamics of irreversible processes is restricted to the domain of validity of linear phenomenological laws (like Fourier's law) (see Chapter V, § 1). In the case of chemical reactions the reaction rate must be sufficiently slow so as not to disturb the Maxwell equilibrium distribution of velocities of each component to any appreciable extent. This excludes only reactions with abnormally low energies of activation (of the order of a few RT).

Let us now compare these general requirements, which must be fulfilled in order to use a macroscopic treatment at all, with the assumptions we have made in the study of stationary non-equilibrium states (Chapter VI). We assumed (cf. pages 86, 87, and 91):

a) Linear phenomenological laws

b) Validity of Onsager's reciprocity relations

c) Phenomenological coefficients may be treated as constants.

These conditions are more restrictive than the conditions of validity in Gibbs formula, quoted above. In the case of chemical reactions, linear phenomenological laws may not be sufficiently good approximations (see Chapter V, § 1). In transport processes it may also be necessary to take into account the variation of the phenomenological coefficients (for example, the variation of the coefficient of thermal conductivity with temperature). How can we introduce such effects in the treatment we have used? These effects may be considered to be non-linear, because they destroy the linear phenomenological equations, or transform the macroscopic equations of change (for example, the Fourier equation for temperature) into a non-linear one. Only recently have some results which belong to the treatment of such effects been published but much remains to be done. It would seem worthwhile, however, to include a preliminary account of these results here, for they indicate the directions in which further progress may be possible.

2. Variation of the Entropy Production

We shall now study the time variation of entropy production with more detail than we did in Chapter VI.

Using the notation (6.26), the entropy production (4.1) becomes

$$\mathcal{P} = \frac{d_i S}{dt} = \sum_k J_k X_k \geq 0 \tag{7.1}$$

Let us decompose the time change $d\mathcal{P}$ into two parts. One is related to the change of the forces and the other to that of the flows. We therefore have

$$d\mathcal{P} = d_X\mathcal{P} + d_J\mathcal{P} = \sum_k J_k dX_k + \sum_k X_k dJ_k \tag{7.2}$$

We shall now prove the following theorems (Glansdorff and Prigogine [63]):

a) Under the restrictive conditions we have enumerated in the first paragraph of this chapter, we have

$$d_X\mathcal{P} = d_J\mathcal{P} = \frac{1}{2} d\mathcal{P} \tag{7.3}$$

The contribution of the time change of the forces to the entropy production is equal to that of the time change of the flows. Indeed (see 4.22),

$$d_X\mathcal{P} = \sum_k J_k dX_k = \sum_{kl} L_{kl} X_l dX_k \tag{7.4}$$

We then use the reciprocity relationships treating the phenomenological coefficients L_{kl} as constants. Therefore,

$$d_X\mathcal{P} = \sum_{kl} X_l (L_{kl} dX_k) = \sum_l X_l dJ_l = d_J\mathcal{P} \tag{7.5}$$

b) In the whole domain of validity of thermodynamics of irreversible processes, the contribution of the time change of the forces to the entropy production is negative or zero. We therefore have the formula

$$d_X\mathcal{P} \leq 0 \tag{7.6}$$

This inequality holds whenever the boundary conditions used are time-independent. The inequality expresses the most general result obtained up to now in thermodynamics of irreversible processes. This entire chapter will be based on formula (7.6). We shall not present a general proof of this inequality but shall only prove it for chemical reactions (Glansdorff and Prigogine [63], Glansdorff [64]). In this case the generalized forces are the affinities A_ρ, while the flows are the chemical reactions v_ρ. The system we consider is an open system in communication with some external phases which are in a time-independent state, and are characterized by given values of temperature, pressure, and chemical potentials. For each component γ one of the following two conditions is realized: either it has a time-independent chemical potential determined by the external reservoirs, or it cannot cross the boundaries of the system. In this way the system will in general be prevented from reaching an equilibrium state. It will then evolve towards a stationary non-equilibrium state.

Let us consider the equation expressing the change in the number of modes of component γ (see formula 1.8)

$$dn_\gamma/dt = (d_e n_\gamma/dt) + \sum_\rho \nu_{\gamma\rho}\mathrm{v}_\rho \tag{7.7}$$

We multiply both members of this equation by the time derivative $\dot{\mu}_\gamma$ of the chemical potential of component γ. We then obtain

$$\dot{\mu}_\gamma(dn_\gamma/dt) = \dot{\mu}_\gamma(d_e n_\gamma/dt) + \sum_\rho \nu_{\rho\gamma}\dot{\mu}_\gamma\mathrm{v}_\rho \tag{7.8}$$

Now let us observe that the first term on the right hand side always vanishes. Indeed we have choosen boundary conditions such that the first factor is zero each time when the second one is different from zero. Now let us sum up this relationship for all components γ. Taking account of the fact that the temperature and the pressure are supposed constant in time, we then obtain,

$$\sum_{\gamma} \dot{\mu}_{\gamma} \frac{dn_{\gamma}}{dt} = \sum_{\gamma\gamma'} \left(\frac{\partial \mu_{\gamma}}{\partial n_{\gamma'}}\right)_{pT} \frac{dn_{\gamma}}{dt} \frac{dn_{\gamma'}}{dt} = \sum_{\gamma\rho} \nu_{\gamma\rho} \dot{\mu}_{\gamma} \mathrm{v}_{\rho} \tag{7.9}$$

Let us introduce the affinity A_{ρ} (see formula 3.34)

$$A_{\rho} = -\sum_{\gamma} \nu_{\gamma\rho} \mu_{\gamma} \tag{7.10}$$

The equation (7.9) may be then written in the simpler form

$$\sum_{\gamma\gamma'} \left(\frac{\partial \mu_{\gamma}}{\partial n_{\gamma'}}\right)_{pT} \frac{dn_{\gamma}}{dt} \frac{dn_{\gamma'}}{dt} = -\sum_{\rho} \mathrm{v}_{\rho} \frac{dA_{\rho}}{dt} \tag{7.11}$$

But the equilibrium stability conditions involve the inequality

$$\sum_{\gamma\gamma'} \left(\frac{\partial \mu_{\gamma}}{\partial n_{\gamma'}}\right)_{pT} x_{\gamma} x_{\gamma'} \geq 0 \tag{7.12}$$

whatever the values of the quantities $x_1, \ldots, x_c$. This is a theorem of classical thermodynamics completely analogous to the theorem which expresses that the specific heat at constant volume or isothermal compressibility are positive. Such inequalities are studied in many textbooks of classical thermodynamics (see for example, [9a]). It is precisely because we still assume here the validity of the fundamental Gibbs formula (3.17) that we can also apply (7.12) because the chemical potentials are then the same functions of the composition as in equilibrium.

Using (7.12), the relation (7.11) gives us

$$T d_X \mathcal{P} = \sum_{\rho} \mathrm{v}_{\rho} dA_{\rho} \leq 0 \tag{7.13}$$

When we combine the expressions (7.3) and (7.6) we return to the theorem of minimum entropy production, as valid in the "linear" region of thermodynamics of irreversible processes. This corresponds to the situation we have studied in the preceding chapters. Here we shall study the case where only relation (7.6) is valid.

3. Velocity Potential

The main difficulty which appears when one tries to use the inequality (7.6) is that it refers to the differential form $d_X \mathcal{P}$ which is *not* a total differential. However, in a case where we deal with one or two independent variables, this difficulty may be easily by-passed (see for more details, Prigogine and Balescu [65]).

Indeed, if we have a single chemical reaction, (7.13) becomes

$$T d_X \mathcal{P} = \mathrm{v}(A) dA = dD \leq 0 \tag{7.14}$$

with

$$\mathrm{v} = \frac{\partial D}{\partial A} \tag{7.15}$$

The function $D(A)$ may be appropriately called a velocity potential. In the stationary state, we have

$$\mathrm{v} = \frac{\partial D}{\partial A} = 0 \tag{7.16}$$

and the thermodynamic stability condition of this state is that D is a minimum

$$\frac{\partial^2 D}{\partial A^2} > 0 \tag{7.17}$$

Indeed, if the minimum condition is not satisfied the slightest fluctuation will permit the system to leave this state (see formula 7.14).

As an example let us consider the reactions

$$A \overset{1}{\rightleftharpoons} X \overset{2}{\rightleftharpoons} B \tag{7.18}$$

We assume that the concentrations of A and B are time independent. Therefore, the total affinity for the two reactions

$$\mathcal{A} = \mathcal{A}_1 + \mathcal{A}_2 = \log \frac{A}{X} + \log \frac{X}{B} \tag{7.19}$$

will also be time independent. (In order to have a less involved notation, we put equal to one, all equilibrium and rate constants, as well as the expression RT; we also signify the components and their concentrations with the same letters.)

For the reaction rates, let us use the following expressions

$$v_1 = X^n(A - X), \qquad v_2 = X^n(X - B) \tag{7.20}$$

We then have

$$T d_X \mathcal{P} = (v_2 - v_1) d\mathcal{A}_2 = (v_2 - v_1) \frac{\partial \mathcal{A}_2}{\partial X} dX$$

$$= X^{n-2}(2X - A - B) dX = dD \tag{7.21}$$

and the velocity potential becomes

$$D = \frac{2}{n+1} X^{n+1} - \frac{1}{n}(A + B)X^n + \text{function independent of } X \tag{7.22}$$

We have two stationary states

$$X = 0 \qquad \text{and} \qquad X = \frac{A + B}{2} \tag{7.23}$$

but while the second corresponds to a minimum of D and therefore to a stable situation, the first corresponds to a maximum of D.

The considerations we just have outlined can be extended to situations where we have two independent variables. We may then introduce an integrating factor $\lambda(A_1, A_2)$ such that

$$\lambda d_X \mathcal{P} = dD \tag{7.24}$$

Unfortunately in the general case of an arbitrary number of independent variables such an integrating factor cannot be found and no velocity potential exists.*

For example, one may verify that no integrating factor exists for the system (see [65])

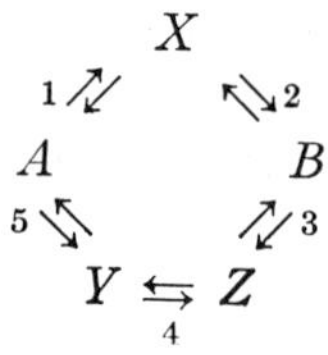

$$\begin{array}{ccccc} & & X & & \\ & {}_1\!\nearrow\!\!\swarrow & & \nwarrow\!\!\searrow_2 & \\ A & & & & B \\ & {}_5\!\nwarrow\!\!\searrow & & \nearrow\!\!\swarrow_3 & \\ & & Y \underset{4}{\leftrightarrows} Z & & \end{array} \tag{7.25}$$

with the reaction rates

$$v_1 = A - X, \qquad v_2 = X - B, \ \ldots, \qquad v_5 = Z - B \tag{7.26}$$

On the contrary, there exists a velocity potential for the system

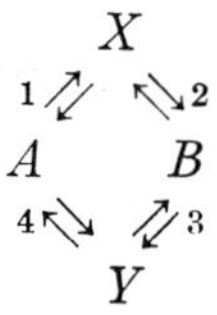

$$\begin{array}{ccccc} & & X & & \\ & {}_1\!\nearrow\!\!\swarrow & & \nwarrow\!\!\searrow_2 & \\ A & & & & B \\ & {}_4\!\nwarrow\!\!\searrow & & \nearrow\!\!\swarrow_3 & \\ & & Y & & \end{array} \tag{7.27}$$

with similar reaction rates.

It may be interesting to represent graphically the velocity fields for these two systems in the affinity space (see Figs. 1 and 2). In both cases we have taken the values of the concentration of A and B equal to 2 and 1. In Fig. 1, we have represented the projection of the veloc-

* Note added in proof: J. C. M. Li has recently shown that $d_X\mathcal{P}$ is always integrable when the entropy production can be separated into individual, *independent* processes [Li, to appear; see also Li, *J. Chem. Phys.*, **29**, 747 (1958)].

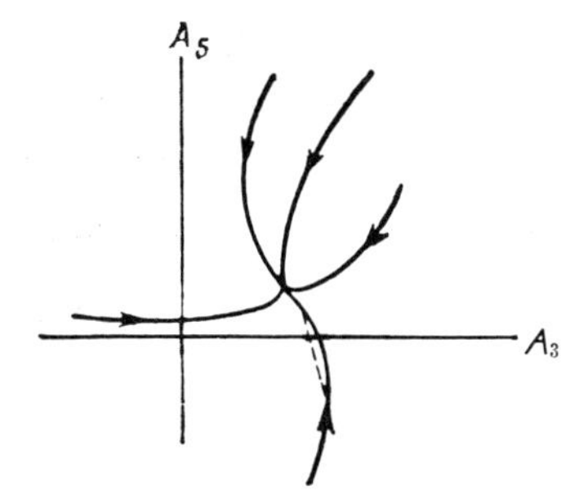

Fig. 1.

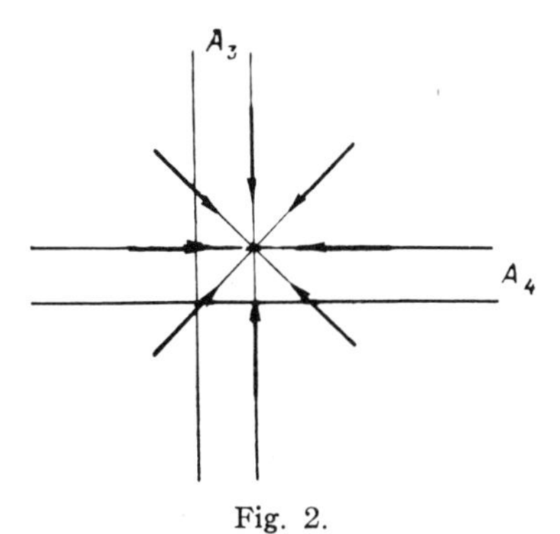

Fig. 2.

ity lines on the plane of affinities A_3A_5. This figure refers to our first example (the non-integrable case). In Fig. 2, which refers to the second example, we use the plane A_3A_4.

One notices the turning motion of the velocity lines in

Fig. 1 which refer to the example in which no velocity potential exists. In the neighborhood of the stationary state two values of A_5 correspond to each value of A_3.

4. General Properties of Non-equilibrium Stationary States

Even in the case in which no velocity potential exists, we may introduce a function which characterizes the behavior of the system in non-equilibrium stationary situations. Formula (7.6) may indeed be used to define a function $\mathfrak{M}$ in the following way (with $\dot{X}_k = dX_k/dt$)

$$\mathfrak{M} = -\frac{d_X \mathcal{P}}{dt} = -\sum_k J_k \dot{X}_k \geq 0 \tag{7.28}$$

This function vanishes for stationary states ($\dot{X}_k = 0$) and is positive everywhere else. The time changes of the forces X_k may be expressed linearly in terms of the flows. The function $\mathfrak{M}$ is therefore a quadratic function of the flows

$$\mathfrak{M} = \sum_{kl} m_{kl} J_k J_l \geq 0 \tag{7.29}$$

For the simple system of chemical reactions (7.25) the function $\mathfrak{M}$ has the following form

$$T\mathfrak{M} = -\sum_{\rho=1}^{\rho=5} \mathrm{v}_\rho \dot{A}_\rho = (A - X)\left[d\left(\log\frac{A}{X}\right)\Big/ dt\right] + \ldots + (Z - B)\left[d\left(\log\frac{Z}{B}\right)\Big/ dt\right] \tag{7.30}$$

$$= \frac{(\mathrm{v}_2 - \mathrm{v}_1)^2}{X} + \frac{(\mathrm{v}_4 - \mathrm{v}_3)^2}{Y} + \frac{(\mathrm{v}_5 - \mathrm{v}_4)^2}{Z}$$

This function appears as an "entropy acceleration" whose sign is determined by the thermodynamic stability conditions. Other variational formulations for non-equilibrium stationary states have been proposed [69, 70]. For example, it has been shown that in the case of the thermal conductivity problem, for time-independent boundary conditions, the average "heat flow" is minimum in the stationary state. But no general formulation, valid for all possible situations, has been obtained until now. However, in all cases which have been analyzed the stationary state is characterized by the minimum of some function quadratic in the rates of the irreversible processes. This function reduces to the entropy production in the linear range.

5. Rotation around Stationary States—Cyclic Processes

We have seen in § 3, that turning motion in the approach to the stationary state is not excluded.

Suppose, for example, we have two independent chemical reactions. Let us develop the rates in terms of the affinities in the neighborhood of the stationary state

$$\begin{aligned} v_a &= L_{aa}\delta A_a + L_{ab}\delta A_b \\ v_b &= L_{ba}\delta A_a + L_{bb}\delta A_b \end{aligned} \tag{7.31}$$

δA_a, δA_b are the differences between the affinities and their values at the stationary state. As an example, we may consider the system

$$A \underset{1}{\rightleftharpoons} X \underset{2}{\rightleftharpoons} Y \underset{3}{\rightleftharpoons} B \tag{7.32}$$

If the concentrations of A and B are maintained as constants in time, we have indeed two independent affinities (for example, A_1 and A_2). The reaction rates v_a and v_b which appear in formula (7.31) may be taken as $v_1 - v_2$ and $v_2 - v_3$ and vanish in the stationary state $v_1 = v_2 = v_3$.

If this stationary state is far from the equilibrium, which corresponds in example (7.32) to a total affinity large in respect to RT, then the phenomenological coefficients which appear in (7.31) no longer satisfy Onsager's relations:

$$L_{ab} \neq L_{ba} \tag{7.32}$$

An extreme case which is interesting to consider is the case in which the matrix L formed by the phenomenological coefficients is purely antisymmetric

$$L_{aa} - L_{bb} = 0, \quad L_{ab} = -L_{ba}$$

then

$$\begin{aligned} \mathrm{v}_a &= L_{ab}\delta A_b \\ \mathrm{v}_b &= -L_{ab}\delta A_a \end{aligned} \tag{7.33}$$

and we have

$$T\mathfrak{M} = -T\frac{d_X\mathcal{P}}{dt} = -L_{ab}\left[\left(\delta A_b \frac{dA_a}{dt}\right) - \left(\delta A_a \frac{dA_b}{dt}\right)\right] \tag{7.34}$$

Let us introduce polar coordinates θ, ρ in the plane A_a, A_b around the stationary state. The expression (7.34) takes the suggestive form

$$T\mathfrak{M} = -L_{ab}\rho^2 \frac{d\theta}{dt} \tag{7.35}$$

We may say that this inequality determines the direction of the rotation around the stationary state [65–67]. Similar results are valid for an arbitrary number of reactions. It should be noticed that a rotation is thermodynamically possible around a non-equilibrium stationary state whereas it would be not permitted around an equilibrium state. This difference originates in the fact that in the first case the entropy production is due mainly to the stationary state itself. The rotation around the stationary state, even if it introduces a negative contribution to the entropy production, is possible as long as the *total* entropy production remains positive.

An interesting example of a rotation around a stationary state has been indicated by Volterra [67]. We shall consider this example in more detail because it brings out very clearly the special features of such a rotation. Moreover, the existence of "rotating" chemical reactions has often been doubted (see [68]).

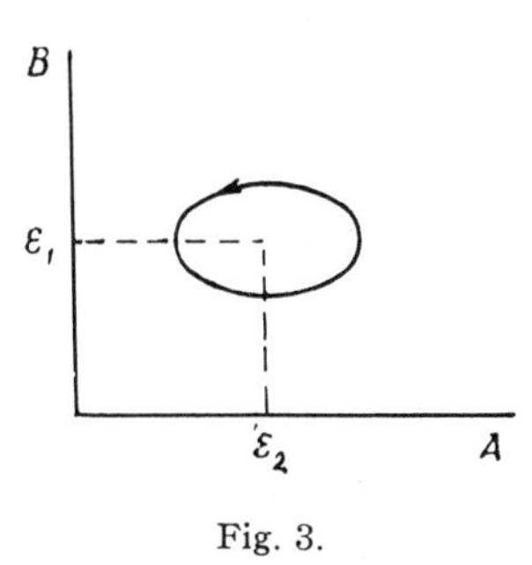

Fig. 3.

Volterra considers the problem of the coexistence of biologic species in a time-independent environment. The simplest case corresponds to the situation in which we have only two species, A and B, such that B "eats" A. The mathematical formulation of this "struggle for life" is then given by the two kinetic equations

$$\frac{dA}{dt} = \epsilon_1 A - AB \qquad (7.36)$$

$$\frac{dB}{dt} = AB - \epsilon_2 B$$

where A and B are the number of animals corresponding to the species A and B and ϵ_1 and ϵ_2 are constants. There exists a stationary state which is determined by the conditions

$$A = \epsilon_2 \qquad B = \epsilon_1 \tag{7.37}$$

However, if the system is not in this stationary state it will describe a closed trajectory around it. These trajectories are always described in the same direction.

These results are easily proved in the neighborhood of the stationary state by linearizing the equations (7.36).

We may now connect Volterra's results to our formula (7.35). Let us indeed take the "chemical system" of reactions

$$\begin{aligned} A + M &\rightarrow 2A \\ A + B &\rightarrow 2B \\ B + M &\rightarrow M' \end{aligned} \tag{7.38}$$

Here M and M' correspond to the biological medium and are maintained as time independent. The affinities are

$$\begin{aligned} A_1 &= \log (M/A) \\ A_2 &= \log (A/B) \\ A_3 &= \log [(BM)/M'] \end{aligned} \tag{7.39}$$

We neglect the rates corresponding to the inverse reactions in (7.38). We therefore have

$$\begin{aligned} \mathrm{v}_1 &= MA \\ \mathrm{v}_2 &= AB \\ \mathrm{v}_3 &= MB \end{aligned} \tag{7.40}$$

Our relation (7.35) now becomes

$$T\mathfrak{M} = -(B - M)(dA/dt) - (M - A)(dB/dt) = \omega \geq 0 \tag{7.41}$$

where ω is the angular velocity of the representative point in its rotation around the stationary state.

6. Stationary States and Time Scales

Volterra's example, which we considered in the preceding paragraph, exhibits clearly a characteristic feature of non-equilibrium stationary states: Such states appear only if there exist two widely separated time scales. For example, in the equations (7.38) we have supposed the concentrations M and M' to be independent. If we had not done this the system would simply have evolved toward the complete thermodynamic equation. But to suppose M and M' time-independent is equivalent to introducing a very long time scale (the "geological scale") in comparison with the time scale related to the evolution of A and B (which is given by the "biological time" scale).

The same considerations are true in the example of thermal diffusion which we considered in Chapters V and VII. There we also have a short time scale which corresponds to the time necessary for the thermal diffusion cell to reach its state for given temperature values of the external heat reservoirs, and a long time scale corresponding to the time necessary for the whole system to reach equilibrium. When we have such a double time scale, evolution towards equilibrium may be separated into two steps. The first corresponds to the appearance of non-equilibrium stationary states and the second to the slow evolution of the stationary states to the complete thermodynamical equilibrium. It is in regions of space where such stationary states occur that we may have a specially high "organization" measured by a low value of the entropy. Therefore such states may be expected to have a special importance from the point of view of evolution of life.

References

1. TH. DE DONDER, *Lecons de Thermodynamique et de Chimie-Physique,* Gauthier-Villars, Paris, 1920.
2. TH. DE DONDER, *L'Affinite,* Gauthier-Villars, Paris, 1928.
3. TH. DE DONDER, *L'Affinite* (second part), Gauthier-Villars, Paris, 1931.
4. TH. DE DONDER, *L'Affinite* (third part), Gauthier-Villars, Paris, 1934.
5. TH. DE DONDER, and P. VAN RYSSELBERGHE, *Affinity,* Stanford University Press, Menlo Park, Calif., 1936.
6. P. DUHEM, *Traité d'Energétique,* Gauthier-Villars, Paris, 1911.
7. P. BRIDGMAN, *The Nature of Thermodynamics,* Harvard University Press, Cambridge, Mass., 1941.
8. M. BORN, *Physik. Zsch.,* **22,** 218 (1921).
9. I. PRIGOGINE and R. DEFAY, *Traité de Thermodynamique*
   a. *Thermodynamique Chimique,* Desoer, Liège, 1950; English translation by D. EVERETT, Longmans Green, London, 1954.
   b. *Tension superficielle et Adsorption,* Desoer, Liège, 1951.
10. J. KIRKWOOD, *J. Chem. Phys.,* **14,** 180 (1946)(cf. also other notes of Kirkwood and his coworkers in subsequent issues of *J. Chem. Phys*).
11. M. BORN, and H. S. GREEN, *Proc. Roy. Soc. A.,* **190,** 455 (1947) (cf. also GREEN, H. S., *Molecular Theory of Fluids.* North Holland Publishing Company, Amsterdam, 1952.)

12. S. Chapman and T. G. Cowling, *The Mathematical Theory of Non-uniform Gases*, Cambridge University Press, New York, 1939.
13. E. A. Guggenheim, *Thermodynamics*, North Holland Publishing Company, Amsterdam, 1949.
14. P. Van Rysselberghe, *Bull. classe sci. Acad. roy. Belg.*, **22**, 1330 (1936); **23**, 416 (1937).
15. J. Needham, *Chemical Embryology*, Cambridge University Press, New York, 1931 (in three volumes).
16. S. R. De Groot and H. A. Tolhoek, *Proc. K. Ned. Acad. Wet.*, **54**(*B*), 41 (1951).
17. I. Prigogine, *Etude Thermodynamique des Phénomenès Irreversibles*, Desoer, Liège, 1947.
18. S. R. de Groot, *Thermodynamics of Irreversible Processes*, North Holland Publishing Company, Amsterdam, 1951.
19. I. Prigogine and P. Mazur, *Physica*, **19**, 241 (1953).
20. Th. De Donder, *Bull. classe sci. Acad. roy. Belg.*, **23**, 936 (1937).
21. I. Prigogine and R. Hansen, *Bull. classe sci. Acad. roy. Belg.*, **28**, 301 (1942); I. Prigogine, *ibid.*, **32**, 30 (1946).
22. J. Meixner, *Ann. Physik*, [5], **41**, 409 (1942); **43**, 244 (1943).
23. P. Mazur, and I. Prigogine, *J. phys. radium*, **12**, 616 (1951).
24. G. Klein, Ph.D. Thesis, University of London, 1951.
25. R. C. Tolman, *The Principles of Statistical Mechanics*, Oxford University Press, New York, 1938.
26. R. H. Fowler, *Statistical Mechanics*, Cambridge University Press, New York, 1936.
27. R. F. Greene, and H. B. Callen, *Phys. Rev.*, **83**, 231 (1951).
28. I. Prigogine, *Physica*, **16**, 137 (1950).
29. S. Chandrasekhar, *Rev. Modern Phys.*, **15**, 1 (1943).
30. A. I. Khinchin, *Statistical Mechanics*, Dover Publications, New York, 1949.
31. H. B. G. Casimir, *Rev. Modern Phys.*, **17**, 343 (1945).
32. P. Curie, *Oeuvres, Société Française de Physique, Paris, 1908.*

33. P. Mazur and S. R. de Groot, *Physica,* **19,** 961 (1953).
34. I. Prigogine, *Physica,* **15,** 272 (1949).
35. F. Lipman, *Adv. Enzymology,* **1,** 99 (1941).
36. I. Prigogine, P. Outer, and Cl. Herbo, *J. Phys. Colloid Chem.,* **52,** 321 (1948).
37. R. Haase and Jost: *Z. physik. Chem.,* **196,** 215 (1950).
38. M. Manes, L. J. E. Hofer, and S. Welles, *J. Chem. Phys.,* **18,** 1355 (1950).
39. J. Meixner, *Z. Naturf.,* **4a,** 594 (1949).
40. P. Mazur and J. Th. G. Overbeek, *Rec. trav. chim. Pays-Bas,* **70,** 83 (1951).
41. K. G. Denbigh, *Nature,* **163,** 60 (1949). K. G. Denbigh and G. Raumann, *Proc. Roy. Soc. A,* **210,** 377, 518 (1951).
42. K. Wirtz, *Z. Physik,* **124,** 482 (1948).
43. S. Weber and G. Schmidt, Commun. Leiden, No. 246a, Rapp. Commun. 7e Congrès Intern. du Froid., The Hague, Amsterdam, 1936.
44. W. H. Keesom, *Helium,* Elsevier, Amsterdam, 1942 (Chap. II).
45. I. Prigogine, *Bull. classe sci Acad. roy. Belg.,* **34,** 930 (1948).
46. S. Harned, *Chem. Rev.,* **40,** 461 (1947).
47. P. and T. Ehrenfest, *Enzykl. Math. Wissensch,* IV, 2 (II) fasc. 6, p. 82, note 23.
48. A. J. Rutgers, Thesis, University of Leyden, 1940.
49. F. Zwicky, *Phys. Rev.,* **43,** 270 (1933).
50. A. J. Lotka, *Proc. Nat. Acad. Sci. U. S.,* **8,** 146 (1922); *Bull. Math. Biophys.,* **10,** 103 (1948).
51. J. Z. Hearon, *Bull. Math. Biophys.,* **12,** 57 (1950).
52. R. Haase, *Z. Naturf.,* **6a,** 420, 522 (1951).
53. P. Mazur, *Bull. classe sci Acad. roy. Belg.,* **38,** 182 (1952).
54. H. J. Schumacher, *Chemische Gasreaktionen,* Steinkopf, Dresden and Leipzig, 1938.
55. J. Z. Hearon, *Bull. Math. Biophys.,* **12,** 135 (1950).

56. I. PRIGOGINE and J. M. WIAME, *Experientia* (Basle), **2,** 451 (1946).
57. L. V. BERTALANFFY, *Naturw.*, **28,** 52 (1940); **32,** 26 (1944); *Das Biologische Weltbild*, Vol. I., Bern, Francke, 1949.
58. G. KLEIN and I. PRIGOGINE, *Physica,* **13,** 74, 89 (1953).
59. P. MAZUR and I. PRIGOGINE. Collection Mémoires in 8°, *Bull. classe sci. Acad. roy. Belg.*, **28,** 1 (1953). I. PRIGOGINE, P. MAZUR, and R. DEFAY, *J. chim. phys.*, **50,** 116 (1953).
60. J. E. VERSCHAFFELT, *Bull. classe sci. Acad. roy. Belg.*, **37,** 853 (1951).
61. R. O. DAVIES, *Physica,* **18,** 182 (1952).
62. L. ONSAGER, *Phys. Rev.*, **37,** 405 (1931); **38,** 2265 (1931).
63. P. GLANSDORFF and I. PRIGOGINE, to appear *Physica,* 1954.
64. P. GLANSDORFF, *Bull. classe sci. Acad. roy. Belg.*, **42,** 628 (1956).
65. I. PRIGOGINE and R. BALESCU, *Bull. classe sci. Acad. roy. Belg.*, **41,** 912 (1955).
66. I. PRIGOGINE and R. BALESCU, *Bull. classe sci. Acad. roy. Belg.*, **42,** 256 (1956).
67. V. VOLTERRA, *Théorie mathématique de la lutte pour la vie,* Gauthier-Villars, Paris, 1931.
68. T. E. BAK, in I. Prigogine, ed., *Advances in Chemical Physics,* Vol. III, Interscience, New York, 1961.
69. I. PRIGOGINE, *Bull. classe sci. Acad. roy. Belg.*, **40,** 421 (1954).
70. T. E. BAK, *J. Phys. Chem.*, **59,** 665 (1955); **60,** 1611 (1956).

List of Symbols[*]

A Chemical affinity (3.26), p. 23

A_ρ Chemical affinity of reaction ρ (3.34), p. 24

$\tilde{A}$ Electrochemical affinity (3.59), p. 31

B Mobility (5.69), p. 72

$C_{p\xi}$ Heat capacity of system at constant pressure and composition (2.8), p. 10

C_γ Molar concentration of component γ (5.9), p. 57

$C_{V\xi}$ Heat capacity of system at constant volume and composition (2.4), p. 10

D Diffusion coefficient (5.71), p. 72

e^* Average energy transferred per unit mass transfer (5.54), p. 68

E Internal energy (2.1), p. 9

f Velocity distribution function, p. 69

f_γ Activity coefficient of γ (3.25), p. 23

F Helmholtz free energy ($= E - TS$), p. 22

$\mathfrak{F}$ Faraday (3.55), p. 30

$\mathfrak{F}_\gamma$ Force (per unit mass) acting on γ (3.72), p. 34

G Gibbs free energy ($= E - TS + pV = H - TS$), p. 22.

h_γ^+ Partial (or specific) enthalpy per unit mass of component γ (2.12), p. 11

h_γ Partial (or specific) molar enthalpy of component γ (2.11), p. 11

$h_{T\xi}$ Latent heat of pressure change at constant temperature and composition (2.8), p. 10

H Enthalpy or heat content function (2.6), p. 10

I Electrical current (3.55), p. 30

J_k Rate or generalized flux of irreversible process k (4.1), p. 40

---

* The name of the symbol is followed by the number of the formula and the page where this quantity is defined or introduced.

k Boltzmann's universal constant, p. 69

$\vec{k}, \overleftarrow{k}$ Rate constants (5.13), p. 57

$K(T)$ Equilibrium constant (5.10), p. 57

$K(p, T)$ Equilibrium constant (3.40), p. 26

$l_{T\xi}$ Latent heat of volume change at constant temperature and composition (2.4), p. 10

L_{ik} Phenomenological coefficient (4.22), p. 45

m_γ Mass of component γ (1.1), p. 4

M_γ Molecular weight of component γ (1.1), p. 4

$\mathfrak{M}$ Entropy production in the linear range (7.28), p. 102

n_γ Number of moles of component γ (1.3), p. 5

$n(\gamma)$ Density of molecules in the internal state γ (3.76), p. 36

N_γ Mole fraction of γ $(= n_\gamma/n)$, p. 22

p Pressure

P Probability (4.33), p. 49

$\mathcal{P}$ Entropy production per unit time (6.26), p. 81

Q Heat received by the system (2.2), p. 9

Q^* Heat of transfer (5.50), p. 67

r_{Tp} Heat of reaction at constant temperature and pressure (2.8), p. 10

r_{TV} Heat of reaction at constant temperature and volume (2.4), p. 10

R Universal gas constant (3.23), p. 22

s_γ Partial (or specific) molar entropy of γ (3.22), p. 22

s_v Entropy per unit volume (3.69), p. 34

S Entropy (3.3), p. 16

t Time

T Absolute temperature

v Velocity (5.58), p. 69

v_γ Partial molar (or specific) volume of γ (3.22), p. 22

v Rate of reaction (1.4), p. 15

v_ρ Rate of reaction ρ (1.7), p. 6

v_v Rate of the chemical reaction per unit volume (3.66), p. 33

$\mathrm{v}(\gamma)$ Reaction rate (3.78), p. 37

v^e Partial rate v at equilibrium, p. 58

$\mathbf{v}$, $\mathbf{v}$	Partial rates of reaction (5.13), p. 57
V	Volume
W	Heat flow (components W^i, $i = x, y, z$) (3.72), p. 34
X_k	Generalized force or affinity of k (4.1), p. 40
α_ρ	Deviation from thermodynamic equilibrium, p. 47
Δ_γ	Diffusion velocity of γ (3.67), p. 34
$\zeta_\gamma(p, T)$	Composition independent part of the chemical potential of γ (3.23), p. 22
$\eta_\gamma(T)$	Composition and pressure independent part of the chemical potential of γ (3.24), p. 22
λ	Thermal conductivity (5.3), p. 55
λ	Lagrange multiplier (6.18), p. 79
μ_γ	Chemical potential of γ (3.18), p. 21
$\overset{+}{\mu}_\gamma$	Chemical potential of γ per unit mass (3.72), p. 34
$\mu(\gamma)$	Chemical potential of molecules in the internal state γ, p. 36
ν_γ	Stoichiometric coefficient of γ (1.1), p. 4
γ_{nu}	Stoichiometric coefficient of γ in reaction ρ (1.5), p. 5
ξ	Degree of advancement or extent of reaction (1.1), p. 4
ξ_ρ	Degree of advancement or extent of reaction ρ (1.5), p. 5
ρ	Density, p. 33
ρ_γ	Density of γ (3.66), p. 33
σ	Entropy production per unit volume and unit time (3.69), p. 34
σ^*	Entropy production per unit volume of the internal space (3.81), p. 38
$\sigma(T)$	Temperature independent part of the entropy (6.48), p. 85
τ	Relaxation time (5.24), p. 60
φ	Electrical potential (3.56), p. 30
φ	Free path (5.4), p. 56
Φ	Resultant flow of energy (2.13), p. 11
Φ	Flow of entropy (3.69), p. 34
ω	Velocity (3.63), p. 33
ω_γ	Velocity of γ (3.65), p. 33

Index